Oxford Children's Picture Dictionary

牛津初級英漢圖畫字典

L. A. Hill and Charles Innes

Illustrated by Barry Rowe

Oxford University Press

啓思出版有限公司

出　版：啓思出版有限公司　牛津大學出版社附屬機構
總發行：牛津大學出版社　香港鰂魚涌糖廠街和域大廈
承　印：海光印刷有限公司　香港鰂魚涌船塢里 8 號

Contents
目次

1 into space
進入太空

2 in the country
在郊外

3 on the farm
在農場

4 in the town
在市鎮

5 in the supermarket
在超級市場

6 in the street
在街上

7 fruit and vegetables
水果和蔬菜

8 in the park
在公園

9 in the classroom
課室裏

10 the house . . .
房子……

11 . . . and garden
……及花園

12 in the kitchen
在廚房

13 at the table
餐桌上

14 the living-room
起居室

15 the hall
門廳

16 a bedroom at night
晚上的睡房裏

17 a bedroom in the day
白天的睡房裏

18 the bathroom
浴室

19 making things
做手工

20 from the post office
從郵政局出來

21 at the birthday party
生日會上

22 my body
我的身體

23 my head
我的頭

24 the family
家庭

25 clothes
衣着

26 at the fire
火警

27 bad weather
惡劣的天氣

28 holiday at the seaside
海邊度假

29 on the sea
在海上

30 in the sky
在空中

31 to the rescue
救援

32 at the hospital
醫院裏

33 bad luck
不幸

34 sport
運動

35 sport
運動

36 sport
運動

37 by road
在路上

38 at the zoo
在動物園

39 large and small animals
大小動物

40 music
音樂

41 helping
幫忙

42 having fun
尋樂趣

43 doing things
活動

44 where are we?
我們在哪裏？

45 where are they going?
他們往哪裏去？

46 pairs
對比

47 pairs
對比

48 what time is it?
幾點鐘？

49 what is the date?
什麼日期？

50 colours
顏色

51 numbers
數目

index
索引

怎樣用這本字典

　　本書所有英文生字都分門別類地編排在一起。要查閱某一物品的英文名稱，先要查目錄，看看哪一頁插圖收有你要找的字，例如：所有運動的名稱，都會列在「運動」的插圖頁裏，插圖裏的運動都編有號碼，憑着號碼便可以找到你要找的字，你還可以利用本書附有的盒式錄音帶，練習這字的讀音。找到你需要的字後，可以試試學習一些在同一頁的其他有關生字，然後把生字蓋起來，看看能記得多少。

　　本書後面編有一個英文索引及一個中文索引，英文索引以字母排列，中文索引則以筆畫順序；每個字之後都列出兩個號碼，例如 **38/2**，第一個號碼表示頁數，第二個號碼表示生字所指的物件的圖樣。

into space 1

1 rocket
火箭

2 space-shuttle
太空穿梭機

3 sun
太陽

4 astronaut
太空人

5 space-suit
太空衣

6 moon
月亮

7 orbit
運行軌道

8 earth/world
地球

9 satellite
人造衞星

10 planet
行星

11 star
星

12 launch-pad
發射台

13 space-station
太空基地

14 control-room
控制室

15 capsule
太空艙

2 in the country　在郊外

1 mountain
山

2 lake
湖

3 valley
山谷

4 forest
森林

5 hill
小山丘

6 village
鄉村

7 river
河流

8 wood
樹林

9 field
田

10 farm
農場

11 path
小徑

12 caravan
篷車

13 tent
帳幕

14 stream
小溪

15 pond
池塘

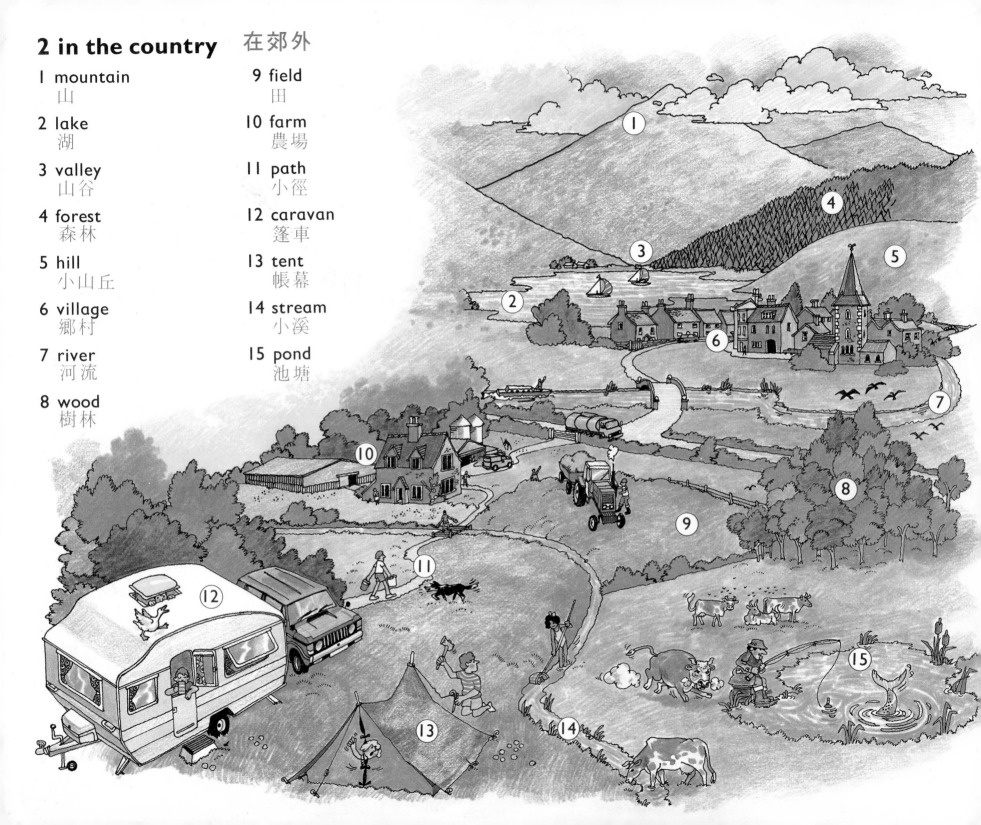

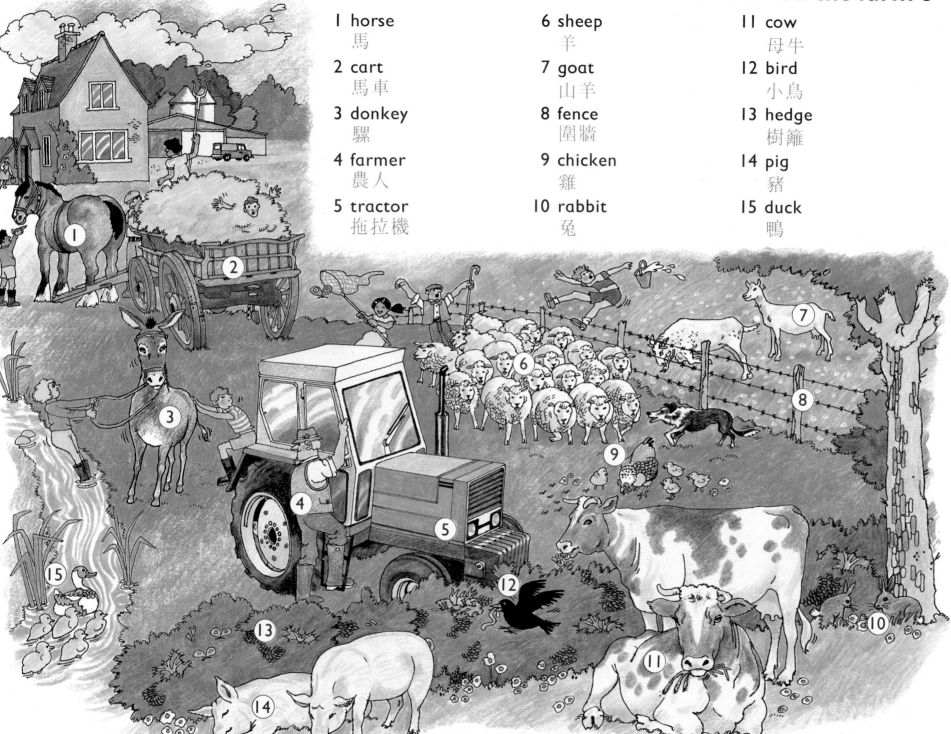

在農場 **on the farm 3**

1 horse
馬

2 cart
馬車

3 donkey
騾

4 farmer
農人

5 tractor
拖拉機

6 sheep
羊

7 goat
山羊

8 fence
圍牆

9 chicken
雞

10 rabbit
兔

11 cow
母牛

12 bird
小鳥

13 hedge
樹籬

14 pig
豬

15 duck
鴨

4 in the town 在市鎮

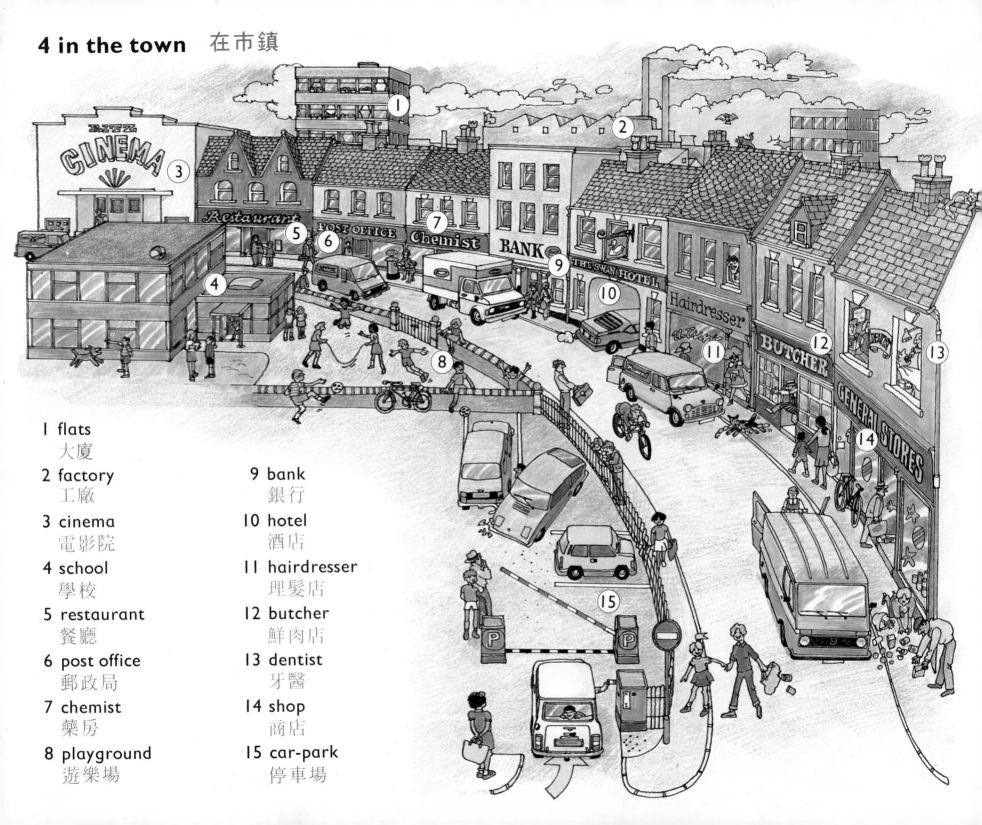

1 flats
大廈

2 factory
工廠

3 cinema
電影院

4 school
學校

5 restaurant
餐廳

6 post office
郵政局

7 chemist
藥房

8 playground
遊樂場

9 bank
銀行

10 hotel
酒店

11 hairdresser
理髮店

12 butcher
鮮肉店

13 dentist
牙醫

14 shop
商店

15 car-park
停車場

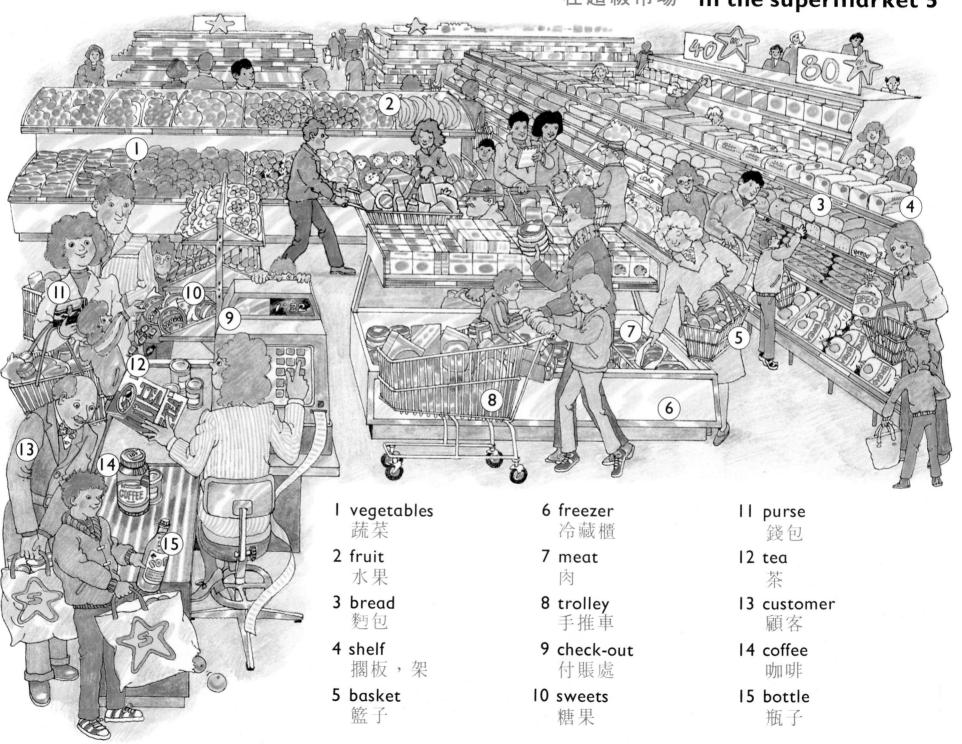

1 vegetables 蔬菜	6 freezer 冷藏櫃	11 purse 錢包
2 fruit 水果	7 meat 肉	12 tea 茶
3 bread 麵包	8 trolley 手推車	13 customer 顧客
4 shelf 擱板，架	9 check-out 付賬處	14 coffee 咖啡
5 basket 籃子	10 sweets 糖果	15 bottle 瓶子

6 in the street 在街上

1 police-station
　警署
2 corner
　街角
3 lorry
　貨車
4 petrol-station
　汽油站
5 petrol-pump
　汽油泵

6 lamp-post
　燈柱
7 telephone-box
　電話亭
8 bus-stop
　公共汽車停車站
9 road
　路
10 bus
　公共汽車

11 (pedestrian) crossing
　行人過路處
12 traffic-light
　交通燈
13 crossroads
　十字路口
14 van
　小型貨車
15 pavement
　行人路

水果和蔬菜　**fruit and vegetables 7**

1 apples
蘋果

2 pears
梨

3 grapes
葡萄

4 bananas
香蕉

5 pineapple
菠蘿

6 oranges
橙

7 lemons
檸檬

8 lettuces
生菜

9 cabbages
椰菜

10 cucumbers
青瓜

11 beans
豆

12 carrots
胡蘿蔔

13 potatoes
馬鈴薯

14 onions
洋葱

15 nuts
堅果

8 in the park 在公園

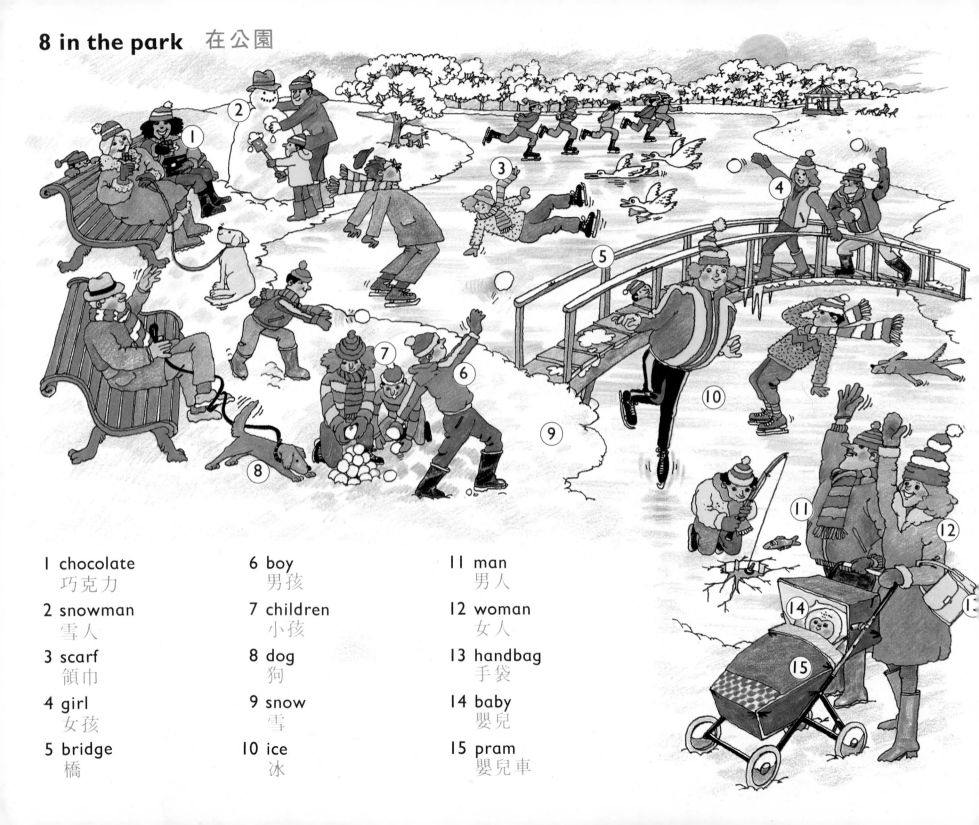

1 chocolate
巧克力

2 snowman
雪人

3 scarf
領巾

4 girl
女孩

5 bridge
橋

6 boy
男孩

7 children
小孩

8 dog
狗

9 snow
雪

10 ice
冰

11 man
男人

12 woman
女人

13 handbag
手袋

14 baby
嬰兒

15 pram
嬰兒車

課室裏 **in the classroom 9**

1 map
地圖

2 teacher
教師

3 chalk
粉筆

4 blackboard
黑板

5 pupil
學生

6 bookcase
書架

7 book
書本

8 desk
書桌

9 exercise-book
練習簿

10 ruler
尺

11 bag
提袋

12 rubber
橡皮

13 pencil
鉛筆

14 pen
筆

15 satchel
書包

10 the house . . . 房子 . . .

1 aerial
天線

2 chimney
烟囱

3 roof
屋頂

4 upstairs
在樓上

5 window
窗

6 pipe
管

7 brick
磚

8 downstairs
在樓下

9 door
門

10 garage
車房

11 dustbin
垃圾桶

12 footpath
小徑

13 gate
柵門

14 washing-line
晾衣繩

15 shed
工具房

1 tree
樹

2 branch
樹枝

3 leaf
樹葉

4 (rope-)ladder
（繩）梯

5 bush
矮樹

6 swing
鞦韆

7 fence
圍牆

8 see-saw
蹺蹺板

9 slide
滑梯

10 grass
草

11 wheel-barrow
獨輪車

12 flower
花

13 (flower-)pot
（花）盆

14 fork
草叉

15 spade
鏟

12 in the kitchen　在廚房

1 cooker
爐

2 grill
烤架

3 oven
烤爐

4 washing-machine
洗衣機

5 can
罐頭

6 cheese
乳酪，芝士

7 fridge
電冰箱

8 frying-pan
煎鍋

9 pan
鍋

10 kettle
燒水壺

11 sink
洗碗盆

12 coffee-pot
咖啡壺

13 milk
牛奶

14 egg
蛋

15 (electric) mixer
(電動)拌和機

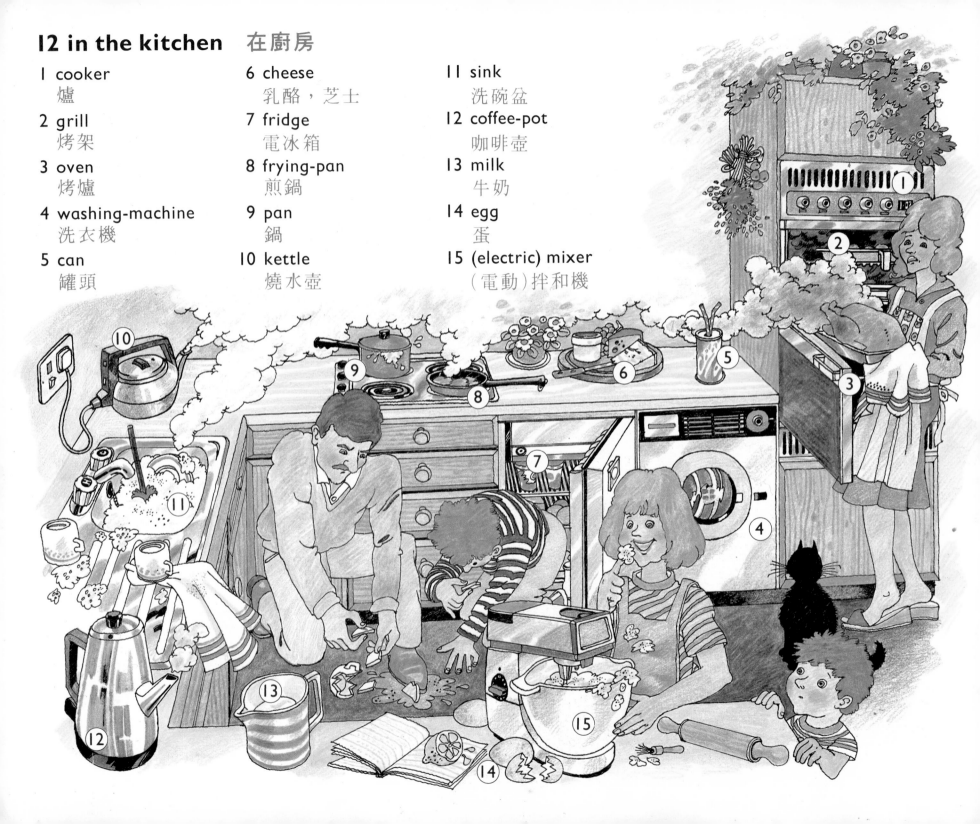

餐桌上 **at the table 13**

1 mug
（無托）杯

2 jug
壺

3 fork
叉

4 dining-table
餐檯

5 plate
碟

6 salt
鹽

7 pepper
胡椒粉

8 spoon
匙

9 bowl
碗

10 knife
刀

11 butter
奶油，牛油

12 jam
果醬

13 toast
烤麵包片

14 glass
玻璃杯

15 chair
椅子

14 the living-room 起居室

1 lamp
座燈

2 television
電視機

3 fireplace
火爐

4 (knitting-)needle
（織）針

5 sofa
沙發

6 cushion
椅墊

7 teapot
茶壺

8 cup
杯

9 saucer
茶杯碟

10 tray
托盤

11 waste-paper basket
字紙簍

12 armchair
靠手椅

13 wool
毛線

14 stool
凳

15 radio
收音機

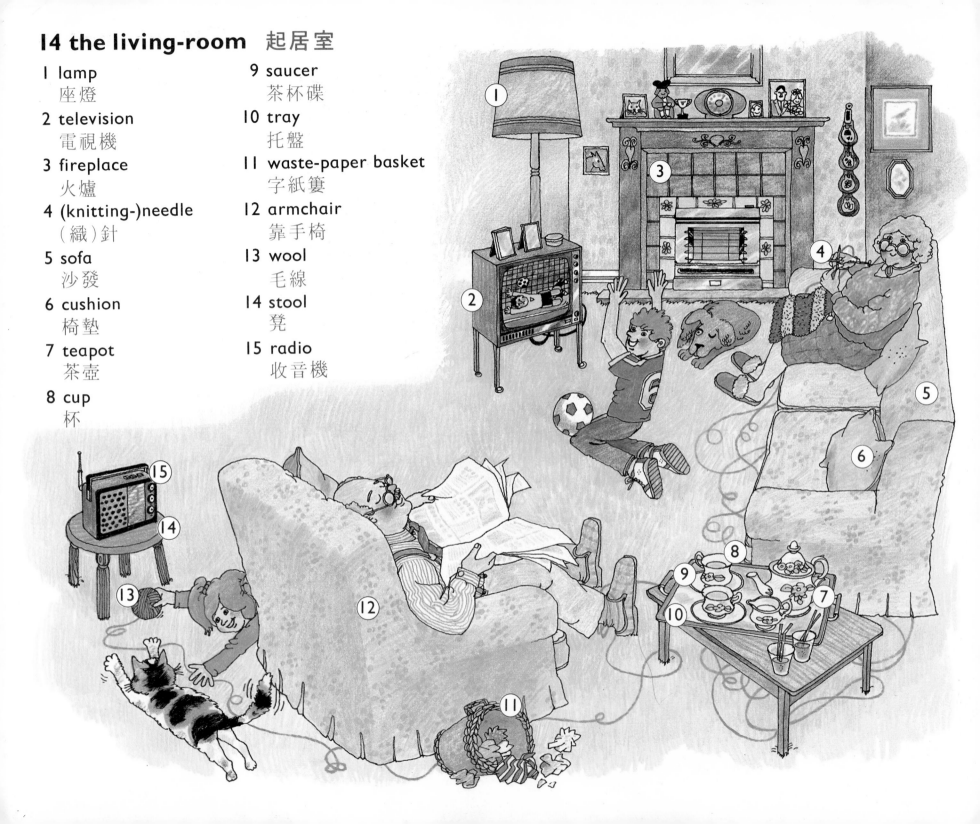

門廳　**the hall 15**

1 ceiling
天花板

2 wall
牆

3 light
燈

4 picture
畫

5 (light-)switch
（燈）開關

6 plant
植物

7 telephone
電話

8 staircase
樓梯

9 cupboard
櫥櫃

10 cardboard box
紙皮盒

11 vacuum-cleaner
吸塵機

12 carpet
地毯

13 brush
刷子

14 dustpan
畚箕

15 floor
地板

16 a bedroom at night 晚上的睡房裏

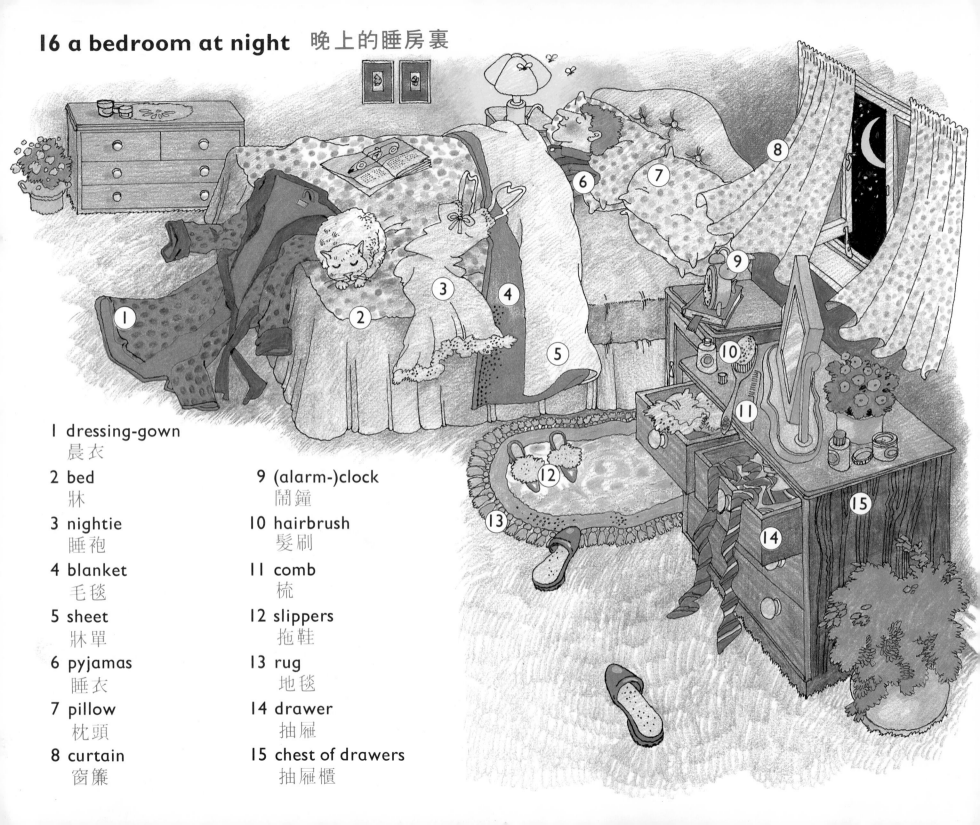

1 dressing-gown
晨衣

2 bed
牀

3 nightie
睡袍

4 blanket
毛毯

5 sheet
牀單

6 pyjamas
睡衣

7 pillow
枕頭

8 curtain
窗簾

9 (alarm-)clock
鬧鐘

10 hairbrush
髮刷

11 comb
梳

12 slippers
拖鞋

13 rug
地毯

14 drawer
抽屜

15 chest of drawers
抽屜櫃

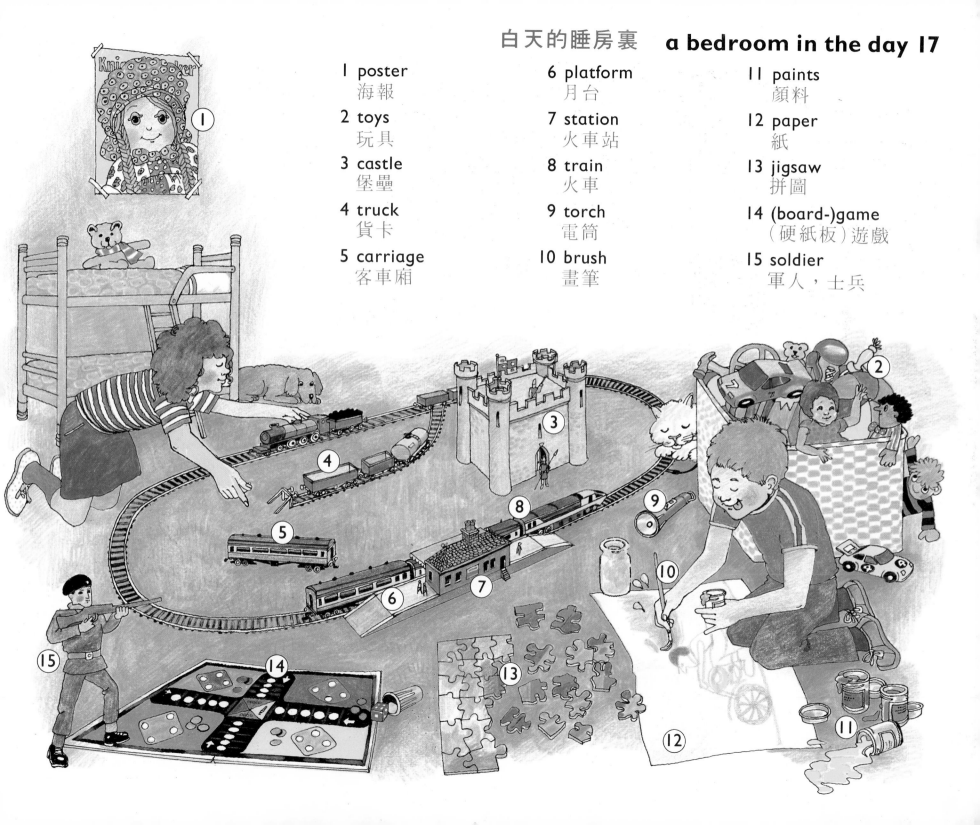

1 poster
海報

2 toys
玩具

3 castle
堡壘

4 truck
貨卡

5 carriage
客車廂

6 platform
月台

7 station
火車站

8 train
火車

9 torch
電筒

10 brush
畫筆

11 paints
顏料

12 paper
紙

13 jigsaw
拼圖

14 (board-)game
（硬紙板）遊戲

15 soldier
軍人，士兵

18 the bathroom 浴室

1 lavatory/toilet
厠所

2 lavatory-/toilet-paper
厠紙

3 mirror
鏡子

4 toothbrush
牙刷

5 tap
水龍頭

6 toothpaste
牙膏

7 basin
洗手盆

8 towel
毛巾

9 scales
磅

10 bathmat
浴室地墊

11 shower
花灑

12 soap
肥皂

13 shampoo
洗髮劑

14 bath
浴缸

15 sponge
海綿

1 iron
熨斗

2 pin
大頭針

3 sewing-machine
縫紉機

4 scissors
剪刀

5 cotton
線

6 button
鈕扣

7 zip
拉鍊

8 doll's house
洋娃娃屋

9 saw
鋸

10 penknife
小刀

11 glue
膠水

12 screw
螺絲釘

13 screwdriver
螺絲起子

14 nail
釘

15 hammer
錘子

20 from the post office 從郵政局出來

1 letter
信

2 postman
郵差

3 string
繩

4 postcard
明信片

5 parcel
包裹

6 letter-box/post-box
郵筒

7 name
姓名

8 address
地址

9 stamp
郵票

10 brake
煞車

11 pump
打氣筒

12 bicycle/bike
腳踏車

13 wheel
車輪

14 tyre
輪胎

15 milk
牛奶

生日會上 **at the birthday party 21**

1 friend
朋友

2 present
禮物

3 biscuit
餅乾

4 camera
攝影機

5 puppet
木偶

6 doll
洋娃娃

7 game
遊戲

8 balloon
氣球

9 ice-cream
冰淇淋

10 candle
蠟燭

11 cake
蛋糕

12 slice
蛋糕片

13 record
唱片

14 record-player
唱機

15 card
卡片

22 my body 我的身體

1 hand
手

2 face
臉

3 chest
胸

4 tummy
腹

5 finger
手指

6 thumb
大拇指

7 arm
手臂

8 head
頭

9 elbow
肘

10 back
背

11 bottom
臀部

12 knee
膝

13 leg
腿

14 foot
腳

15 toe
腳趾

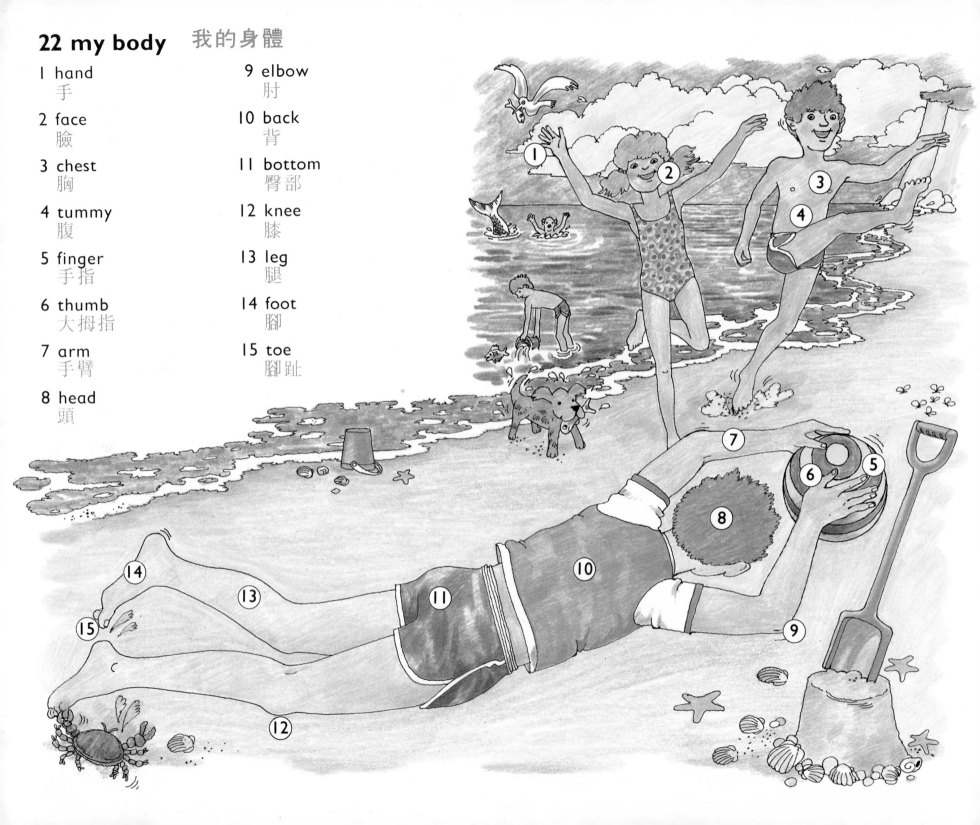

1 chin
下巴

2 eyebrow
眼眉

3 tongue
舌頭

4 beard
鬍鬚

5 mouth
口，嘴巴

6 hair
頭髮

7 nose
鼻

8 moustache
髭（嘴上的鬍子）

9 ear-ring
耳環

10 eye
眼

11 neck
頸

12 cheek
面頰

13 lip
唇

14 tooth
牙齒

15 ear
耳

24 the family 家庭

1 grandfather
祖父

2 grandmother
祖母

3 father/daddy
父親

4 mother/mummy
母親

5 brother
兄弟

6 sister
姊妹

7 uncle
叔,伯,舅父,姑丈,姨丈

8 aunt
嬸母,舅母,姑母,姨母

9 cousin
表親

10 husband
丈夫

11 wife
妻子

12 son
兒子

13 daughter
女兒

1 T-shirt
　汗衫

2 trousers
　長褲

3 sock
　襪

4 vest
　背心

5 pants
　內褲

6 shorts
　短褲

7 dress
　衣連裙

8 sweater
　毛線衫

9 jacket
　外衣

10 jeans
　牛仔褲

11 pocket
　口袋

12 skirt
　裙

13 shoelace
　鞋帶

14 shoe
　鞋

15 shirt
　襯衫

26 at the fire 火警

1 fireman
消防員

2 smoke
烟

3 ladder
雲梯

4 fire-escape
太平梯

5 fire
火

6 building
建築物

7 water
水

8 fire-engine
救火車

9 ambulance
救護車

10 crowd
人羣

11 police-car
警車

12 policeman
警察

13 (fire-)hose
消防水管

14 axe
斧

15 bell
鐘

1 rainbow
天虹

2 sky
天空

3 cloud
雲

4 lightning
閃電

5 rain
雨

6 hat
帽

7 wind
風

8 belt
衣帶

9 coat
大衣

10 glove
手套

11 cap
軟帽

12 umbrella
雨傘

13 raincoat
雨衣

14 boot
膠套靴

15 puddle
小髒水潭

28 holiday at the seaside 海邊度假

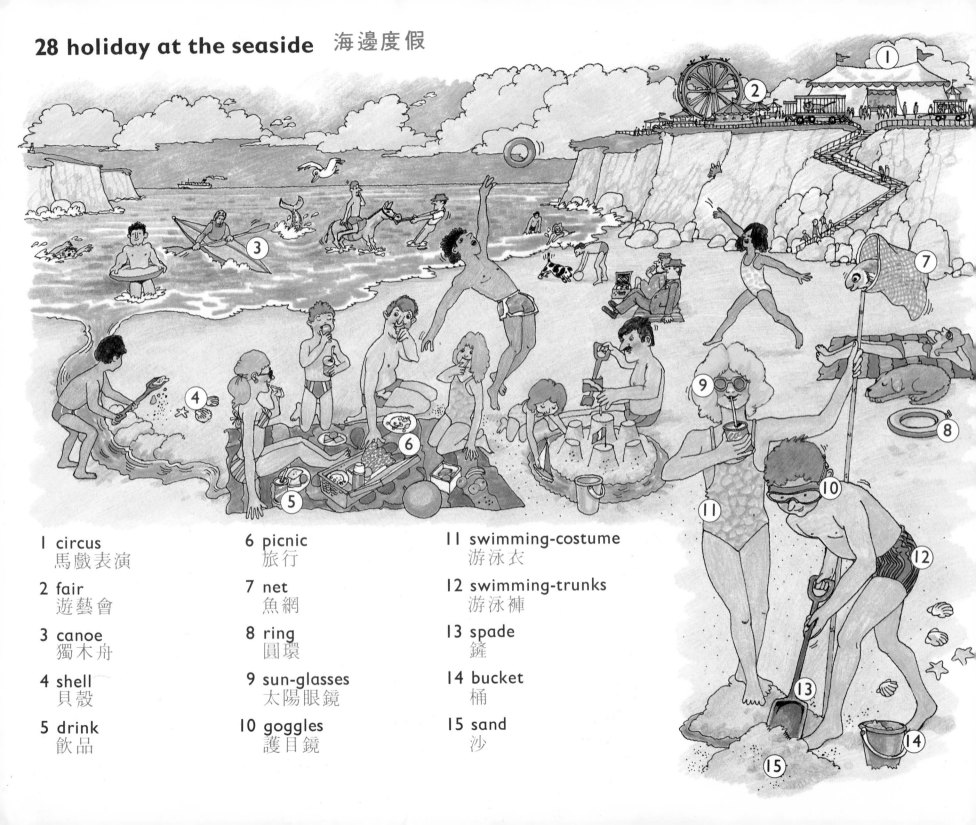

1 circus
馬戲表演

2 fair
遊藝會

3 canoe
獨木舟

4 shell
貝殼

5 drink
飲品

6 picnic
旅行

7 net
魚網

8 ring
圓環

9 sun-glasses
太陽眼鏡

10 goggles
護目鏡

11 swimming-costume
游泳衣

12 swimming-trunks
游泳褲

13 spade
鏟

14 bucket
桶

15 sand
沙

1 fishing-boat 漁船	**6 container-ship** 貨櫃船	**11 raft** 木筏
2 tanker 油船	**7 submarine** 潛水艇	**12 motor-boat** 摩托船
3 flag 旗	**8 ferry** 渡船	**13 lifeboat** 救生艇
4 liner 郵輪	**9 land** 陸地	**14 captain** 船長
5 tug 拖船	**10 beach** 海灘	**15 rowing-boat** 舢舨

30 in the sky 在空中

1 glider
滑翔機

2 balloon
氣球

3 parachute
降落傘

4 kite
紙鳶

5 hotel
酒店

6 aeroplane
飛機

7 air hostess
空中小姐

8 airport
機場

9 (jet) engine
噴射引擎

10 wing
機翼

11 helicopter
直升機

12 runway
跑道

13 ticket
票

14 money
錢

15 passenger
乘客

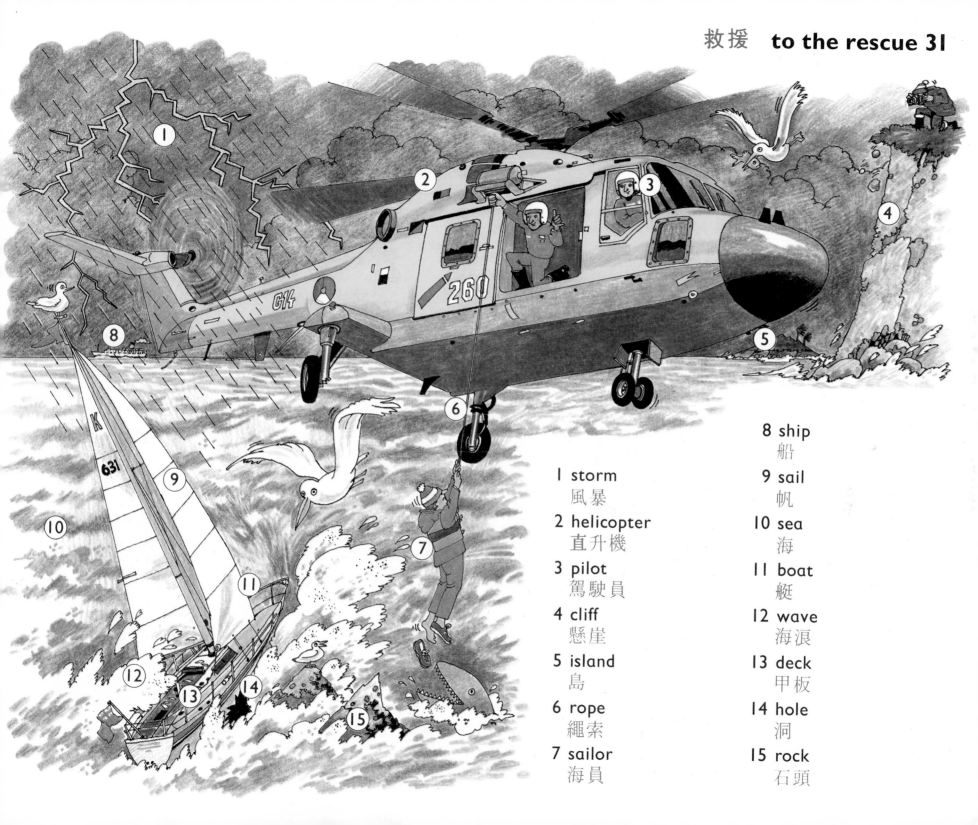

1 storm
風暴

2 helicopter
直升機

3 pilot
駕駛員

4 cliff
懸崖

5 island
島

6 rope
繩索

7 sailor
海員

8 ship
船

9 sail
帆

10 sea
海

11 boat
艇

12 wave
海浪

13 deck
甲板

14 hole
洞

15 rock
石頭

32 at the hospital　醫院裏

1 lift
升降機

2 nurse
護士

3 watch
掛錶

4 handkerchief
手帕

5 glasses
眼鏡

6 doctor
醫生

7 injection
注射

8 newspaper
報紙

9 photograph
相片

10 patient
病人

11 medicine
藥水

12 pills
藥丸

13 bandage
繃帶

14 stretcher
擔架

15 plaster
膠布

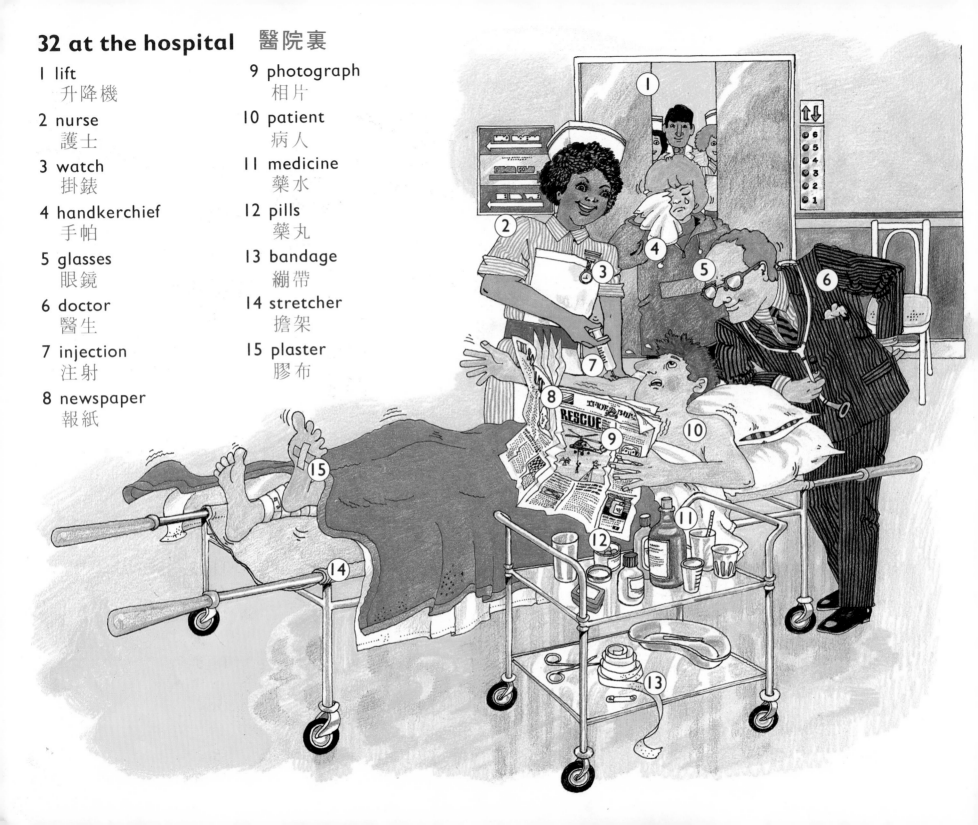

不幸　**bad luck 33**

1 camp
營

2 break
斷

3 fall
跌下

4 stand
站立

5 carry
攜帶

6 lie
躺

7 pick up
拾起

8 cry
哭泣

9 cut
割傷

10 bleed
流血

11 write
寫字

12 sit
坐

13 tear
撕破

14 tie
綁，紮

15 sting
刺痛

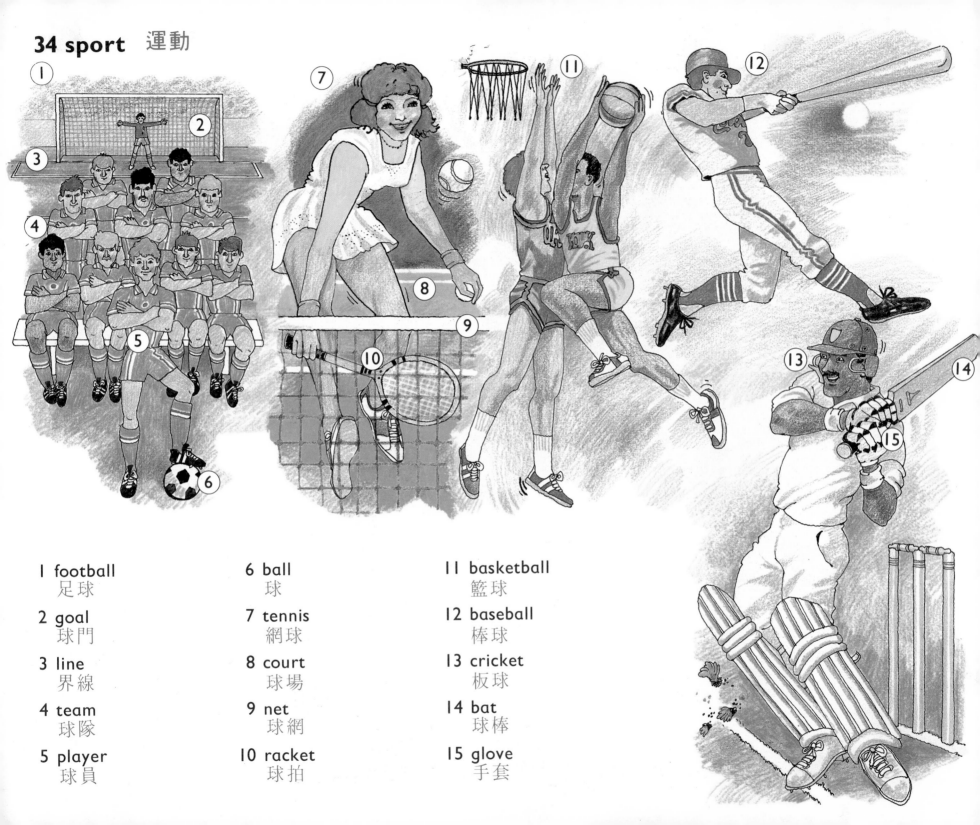

34 sport 運動

1 football
足球

2 goal
球門

3 line
界線

4 team
球隊

5 player
球員

6 ball
球

7 tennis
網球

8 court
球場

9 net
球網

10 racket
球拍

11 basketball
籃球

12 baseball
棒球

13 cricket
板球

14 bat
球棒

15 glove
手套

1 skating
溜冰

2 judo
柔道

3 cycling
騎腳踏車

4 swimming
游泳

5 swimming-pool
游泳池

6 rugby
欖球

7 fishing
釣魚

8 athletics
體育運動

9 boxing
拳擊

10 table tennis
乒乓球

11 motor-racing
賽車

12 ski-ing
滑雪

13 rowing
划艇

14 trainers
運動鞋

15 track suit
運動衣

36 sport 運動

1 dive
跳水

2 sail
揚帆

3 walk
步行

4 ride
騎馬

5 fly
飛行

6 jump
跳高

7 shoot
射

8 kick
踢

9 throw
擲

10 swim
游泳

11 catch
接球

12 drive
駕車

13 pass
傳球

14 hit
擊球

15 run
跑

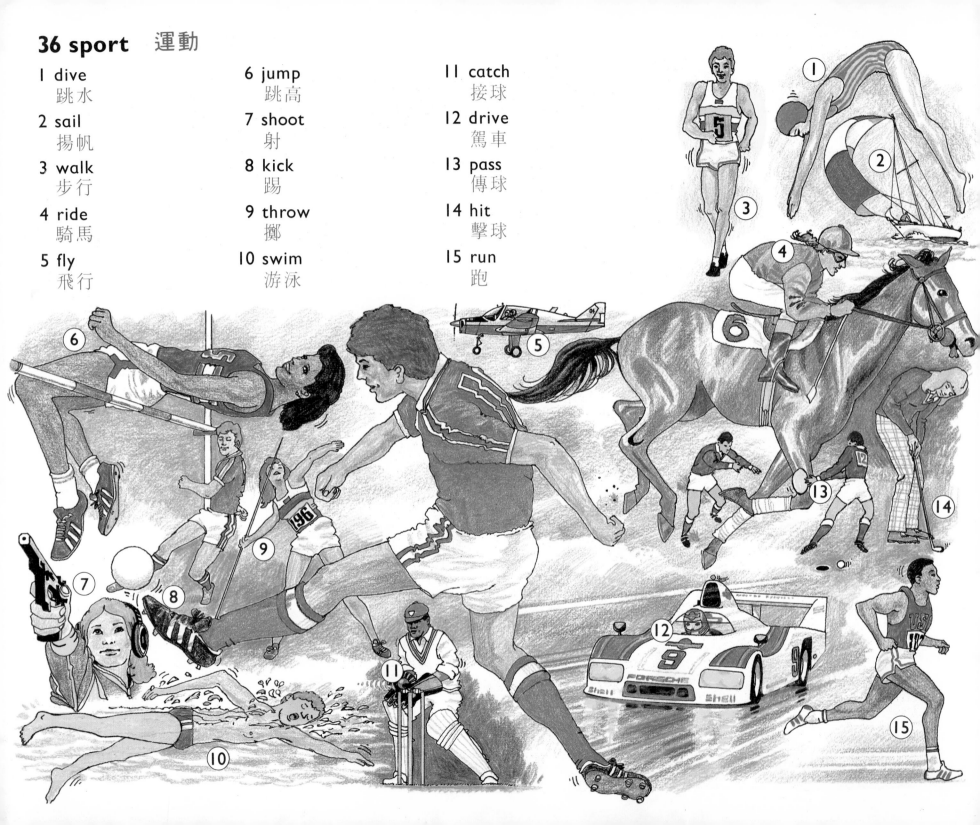

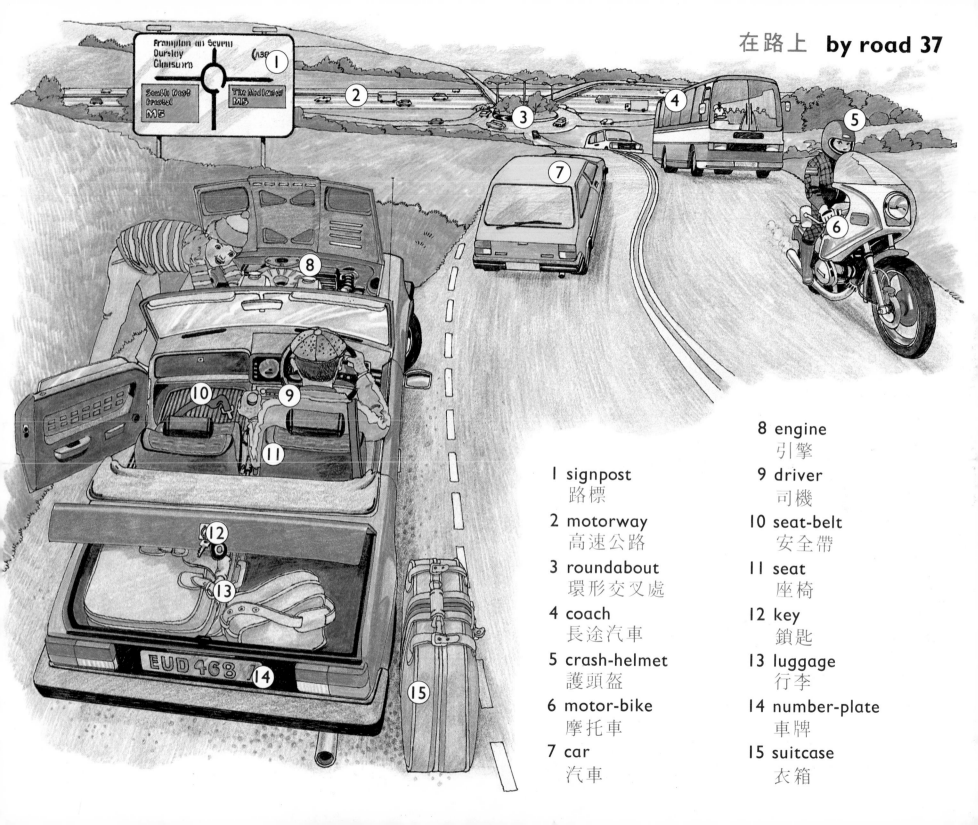

在路上 **by road 37**

8 engine
引擎

1 signpost
路標

9 driver
司機

2 motorway
高速公路

10 seat-belt
安全帶

3 roundabout
環形交叉處

11 seat
座椅

4 coach
長途汽車

12 key
鎖匙

5 crash-helmet
護頭盔

13 luggage
行李

6 motor-bike
摩托車

14 number-plate
車牌

7 car
汽車

15 suitcase
衣箱

38 at the zoo   在動物園

1 eagle
鷹
2 cage
籠
3 tiger
老虎
4 crocodile
鱷魚
5 snake
蛇
6 lion
獅子
7 fish
魚
8 dolphin
海豚
9 camel
駱駝
10 bear
熊
11 elephant
大象
12 keeper
看守員
13 penguin
企鵝
14 monkey
猴子
15 panda
熊貓

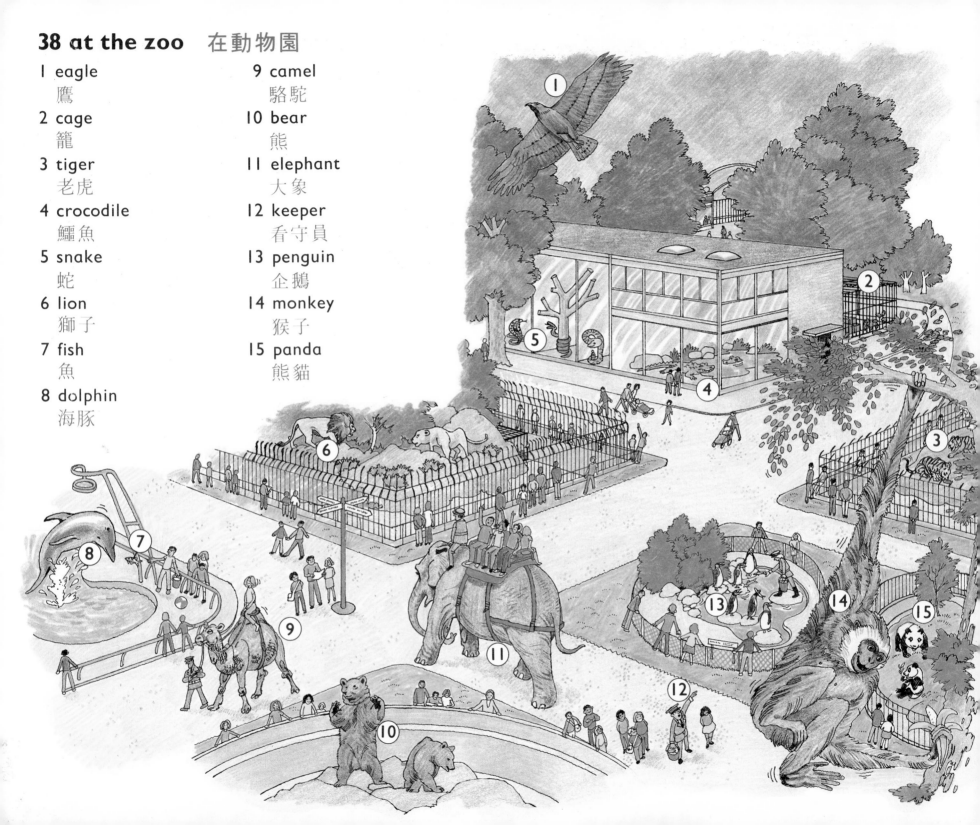

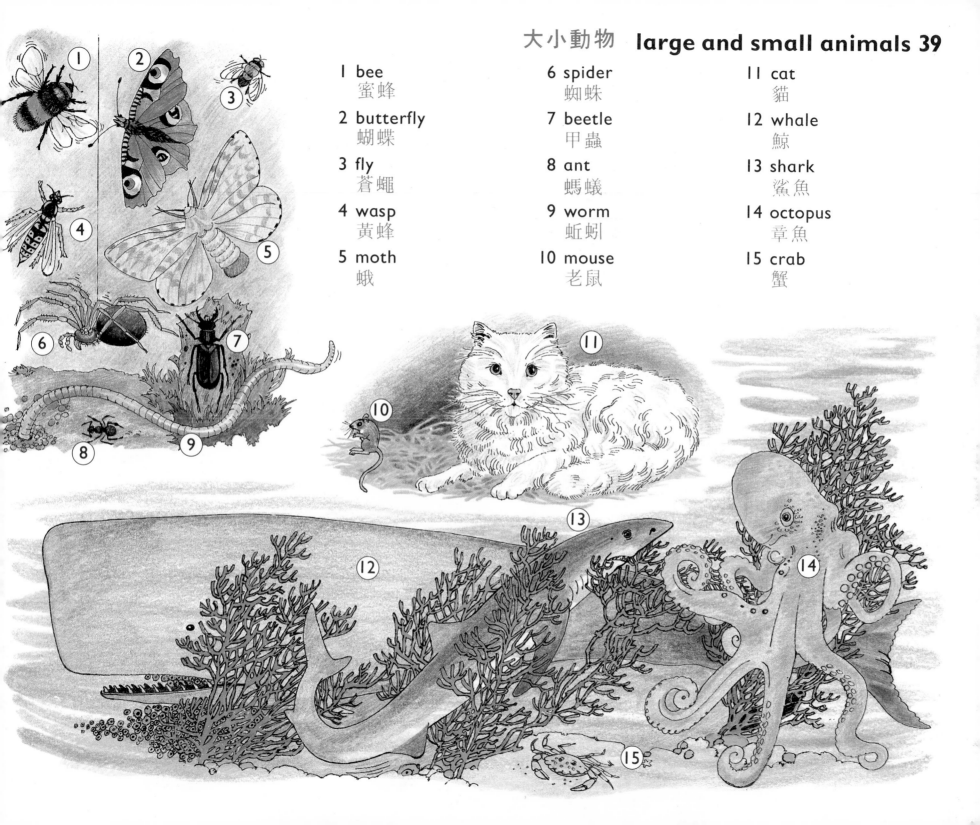

1 bee 蜜蜂	6 spider 蜘蛛	11 cat 貓
2 butterfly 蝴蝶	7 beetle 甲蟲	12 whale 鯨
3 fly 蒼蠅	8 ant 螞蟻	13 shark 鯊魚
4 wasp 黃蜂	9 worm 蚯蚓	14 octopus 章魚
5 moth 蛾	10 mouse 老鼠	15 crab 蟹

40 music 音樂

1 trumpet
喇叭

2 player
樂師

3 violin
小提琴

4 recorder
直笛

5 drum
鼓

6 singer
歌手

7 (pop) group
流行樂隊

8 microphone
麥克風

9 string
弦

10 piano
鋼琴

11 stool
凳

12 guitar
結他

13 cassette
錄音帶

14 music
樂曲

15 record
唱片

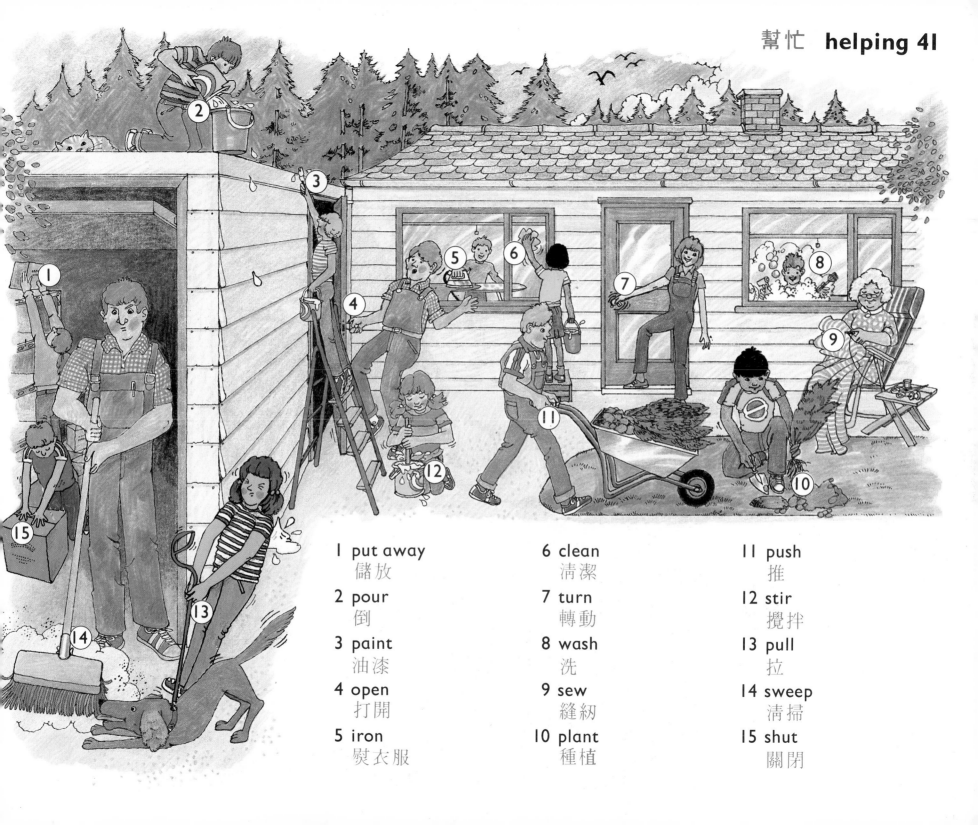

1 put away
儲放

2 pour
倒

3 paint
油漆

4 open
打開

5 iron
熨衣服

6 clean
清潔

7 turn
轉動

8 wash
洗

9 sew
縫紉

10 plant
種植

11 push
推

12 stir
攪拌

13 pull
拉

14 sweep
清掃

15 shut
關閉

42 having fun 尋樂趣

1 wave
揮手

2 kiss
吻

3 laugh
笑

4 swing
擺動

5 clap
拍手

6 shout
呼喊

7 climb
攀爬

8 shake (hands)
握手

9 sing
唱

10 play
玩耍

11 dance
跳舞

12 hug
抱

13 give
給

14 smile
微笑

15 blow
吹

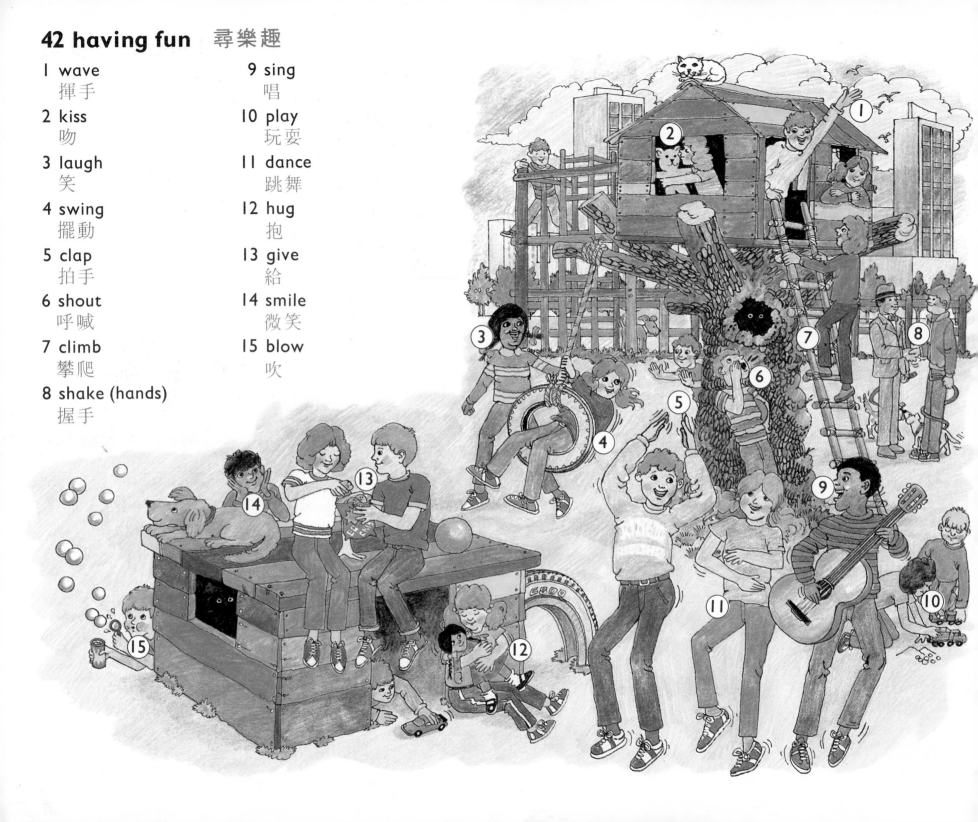

1 brush
刷

2 comb
梳

3 dream
做夢

4 sleep
睡覺

5 wake
醒

6 eat
吃

7 drink
飲

8 bite
咬

9 lick
舔

10 post
投寄

11 read
讀

12 draw
繪畫

13 listen
聽

14 hide
躲藏

15 crawl
爬

44 where are we? 我們在哪裏？

1 **by** the door
在門旁

2 **at the top of** the stairs
在樓梯頂

3 **on** the dinosaur
在恐龍上

4 **in/inside** the dinosaur
在恐龍裏

5 **outside** the window
在窗外

6 **at** the bookstall
在書攤

7 **in front of** the tail
在尾巴前面

8 **behind** the leg
在腿後

9 **at the bottom of** the stairs
在樓梯底下

10 **up**
在上方

11 **down**
在下方

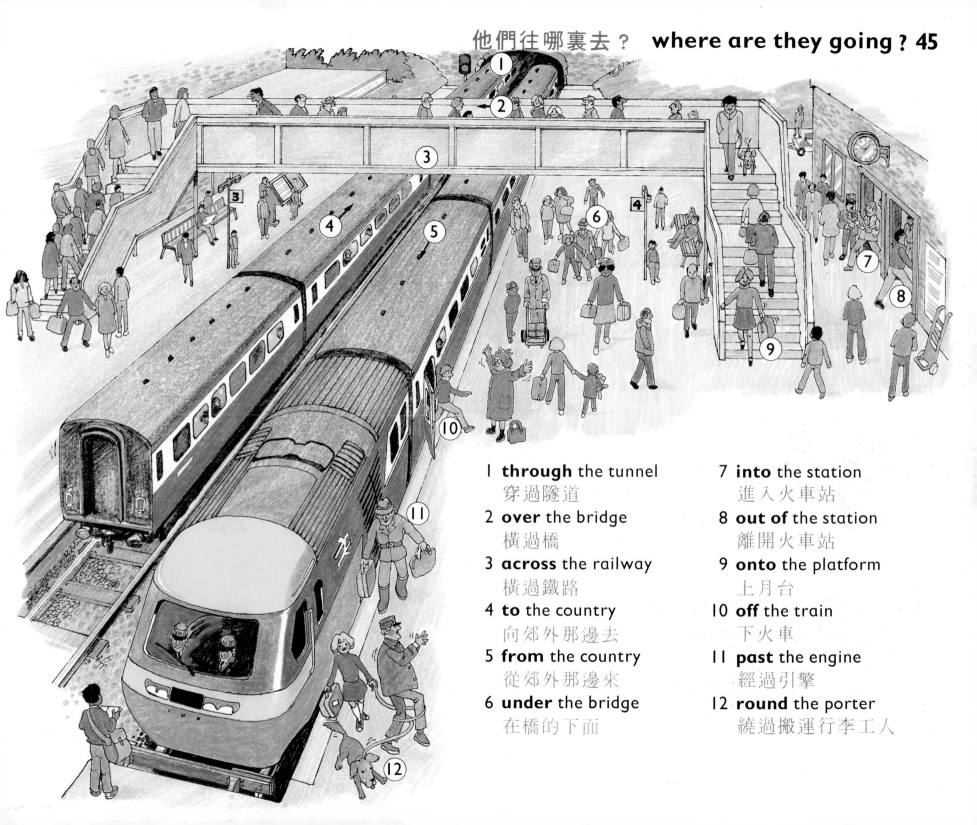

1 **through** the tunnel
穿過隧道

2 **over** the bridge
橫過橋

3 **across** the railway
橫過鐵路

4 **to** the country
向郊外那邊去

5 **from** the country
從郊外那邊來

6 **under** the bridge
在橋的下面

7 **into** the station
進入火車站

8 **out of** the station
離開火車站

9 **onto** the platform
上月台

10 **off** the train
下火車

11 **past** the engine
經過引擎

12 **round** the porter
繞過搬運行李工人

46 pairs 對比

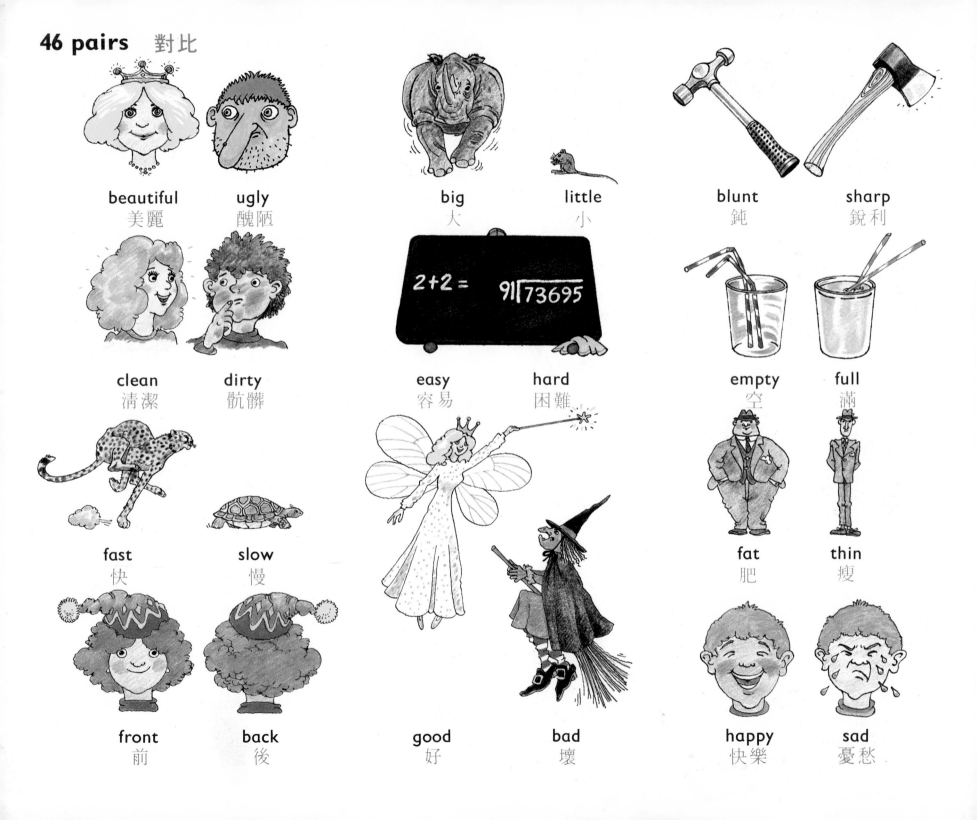

beautiful 美麗 · **ugly** 醜陋

big 大 · **little** 小

blunt 鈍 · **sharp** 銳利

clean 清潔 · **dirty** 骯髒

easy 容易 · **hard** 困難

empty 空 · **full** 滿

fast 快 · **slow** 慢

fat 肥 · **thin** 瘦

front 前 · **back** 後

good 好 · **bad** 壞

happy 快樂 · **sad** 憂愁

heavy 　　light
重 　　　輕

high 　　low
高 　　　矮

hot 　　cold
熱 　　冷

left 　　right
左 　　右

dark 　　light
黑暗 　　光明

short 　　long
短 　　長

old 　　new
舊 　　新

open 　　closed/shut
開着的 　　關閉的

strong 　　weak
強壯 　　虛弱

wet 　　dry
濕 　　乾

young 　　old
少 　　老

48 what time is it? 幾點鐘？

five o'clock
五點鐘

half past four
四點半

quarter past six
六點一刻

quarter to three
兩點三刻

ten to seven
六點五十分

twenty past eight
八點二十分

60 seconds	=	1 minute
秒		分
60 minutes	=	1 hour
分		小時
24 hours	=	1 day
小時		日
7 days	=	1 week
日		星期
4 weeks	=	1 month
星期		月
12 months	=	1 year
月		年

midnight
午夜

noon
正午

months
月份
January
一月
February
二月
March
三月
April
四月
May
五月
June
六月
July
七月
August
八月
September
九月
October
十月
November
十一月
December
十二月

days of the week
星期
Sunday
星期日
Monday
星期一
Tuesday
星期二
Wednesday
星期三
Thursday
星期四
Friday
星期五
Saturday
星期六

50 colours 顏色

pink
粉紅

yellow
黃

blue
藍

green
綠

brown
棕

red
紅

grey
灰

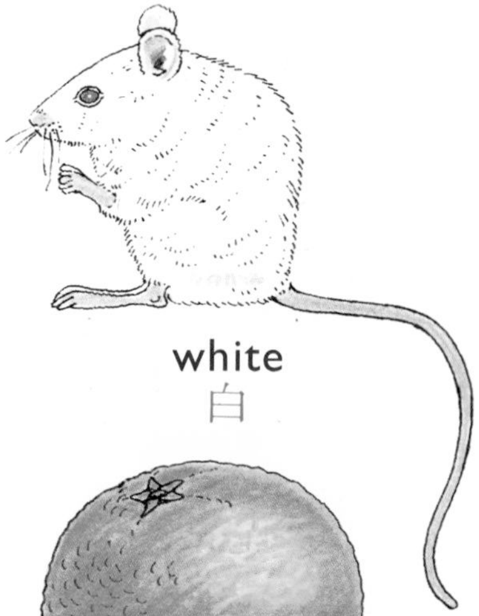

white
白

purple
紫

black
黑

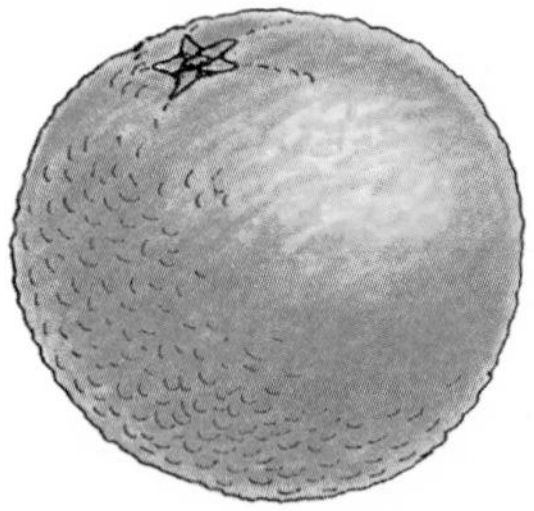

orange
橙

nought/zero
零

one
一

two
二

three
三

four
四

five
五

six
六

seven
七

eight
八

nine
九

ten
十

eleven
十一

twelve
十二

thirteen
十三

fourteen
十四

fifteen
十五

sixteen
十六

seventeen
十七

eighteen
十八

nineteen
十九

twenty
二十

twenty-one
二十一

thirty
三十

forty
四十

fifty
五十

sixty
六十

seventy
七十

eighty
八十

ninety
九十

a/one hundred
一百

a/one thousand
一千

a/one million
一百萬

Index

Page numbers are printed in **thick** type. Numbers in plain type show where to find a word on the page. So 'chair 13/15' means that the word 'chair' is number 15 on page 13.

Aa across **45**/3
address **20**/8
aerial **10**/1
aeroplane **30**/6
air hostess **30**/7
airport **30**/8
alarm-clock **16**/9
ambulance **26**/9
animal **39**
ant **39**/8
apple **7**/1
April **49**
are **44**; **45**
armchair **14**/12
astronaut **1**/4
at **13**; **16**; **21**; **26**; **28**; **32**; **38**; **44**/6
athletics **35**/8
at the bottom of **44**/9
at the top of **44**/2
August **49**
aunt **24**/8
away **41**/1
axe **26**/14

Bb baby **8**/14
back **22**/10; **46**
bad **27**; **33**; **46**
bag **9**/11
ball **34**/6
balloon **21**/8; **30**/2
banana **7**/4
bandage **32**/13
bank **4**/9
baseball **34**/12
basin **18**/7
basket **5**/5
basketball **34**/11

bat **34**/14
bath **18**/14
bathmat **18**/10
bathroom **18**
beach **29**/10
bean **7**/11
bear **38**/10
beard **23**/4
beautiful **46**
bed **16**/2
bedroom **16**; **17**
bee **39**/1
beetle **39**/7
behind **44**/8
bell **26**/15
belt **27**/8
bicycle **20**/12
big **46**
bike **20**/12
bird **3**/12
birthday **21**
biscuit **21**/3
bite **43**/8
black **50**
blackboard **9**/4
blanket **16**/4
bleed **33**/10
blow **42**/15
blue **50**
blunt **46**
board-game **17**/14
boat **31**/11
body **22**
book **9**/7
bookcase **9**/6
bookstall **44**/6
boot **27**/14
bottle **5**/15
bottom **22**/11; **44**/9
bowl **13**/9
box **15**/10
boxing **35**/9
boy **8**/6
brake **20**/10
branch **11**/2
bread **5**/3

break **33**/2
brick **10**/7
bridge **8**/5; **45**/2, 6
brother **24**/5
brown **50**
brush **15**/13; **17**/10; **43**/1
bucket **28**/14
building **26**/6
bus **6**/10
bush **11**/5
bus-stop **6**/8
butcher **4**/12
butter **13**/11
butterfly **39**/2
button **19**/6
by **37**; **44**/1

Cc cabbage **7**/9
cage **38**/2
cake **21**/11
camel **38**/9
camera **21**/4
camp **33**/1
can **12**/5
candle **21**/10
canoe **28**/3
cap **27**/11
capsule **1**/15
captain **29**/14
car **37**/7
caravan **2**/12
card **21**/15
cardboard box **15**/10
car-park **4**/15
carpet **15**/12
carriage **17**/5
carrot **7**/12
carry **33**/5
cart **3**/2
cassette **40**/13
castle **17**/3
cat **39**/11
catch **36**/11
ceiling **15**/1
chair **13**/15
chalk **9**/3

check-out **5**/9
cheek **23**/12
cheese **12**/6
chemist **4**/7
chest **22**/3
chest of drawers **16**/15
chicken **3**/9
children **8**/7
chimney **10**/2
chin **23**/1
chocolate **8**/1
cinema **4**/3
circus **28**/1
clap **42**/5
classroom **9**
clean **41**/6; **46**
cliff **31**/4
climb **42**/7
clock **16**/9
closed **47**
clothes **25**
cloud **27**/3
coach **37**/4
coat **27**/9
coffee **5**/14
coffee-pot **12**/12
cold **47**
colour **50**
comb **16**/11; **43**/2
container-ship **29**/6
control-room **1**/14
cooker **12**/1
corner **6**/2
cotton **19**/5
country **2**; **45**/4, 5
court **34**/8
cousin **24**/9
cow **3**/11
crab **39**/15
crash-helmet **37**/5
crawl **43**/15
cricket **34**/13
crocodile **38**/4
crossing **6**/11
crossroads **6**/13
crowd **26**/10

cry **33**/8
cucumber **7**/10
cup **14**/8
cupboard **15**/9
curtain **16**/8
cushion **14**/6
customer **5**/13
cut **33**/9
cycling **35**/3

Dd daddy **24**/3
dance **42**/11
dark **47**
date **49**
daughter **24**/13
day **17**; **48**; **49**
December **49**
deck **31**/13
dentist **4**/13
desk **9**/8
dining-table **13**/4
dinosaur **44**/3, 4
dirty **46**
dive **36**/1
do **43**
doctor **32**/6
dog **8**/8
doll **21**/6
doll's house **19**/8
dolphin **38**/8
donkey **3**/3
door **10**/9; **44**/1
down **44**/11
downstairs **10**/8
draw **43**/12
drawer **16**/14
dream **43**/3
dress **25**/7
dressing-gown **16**/1
drink **28**/5; **43**/7
drive **36**/12
driver **37**/9
drum **40**/5
dry **47**
duck **3**/15
dustbin **10**/11

dustpan **15**/14

Ee eagle **38**/1
ear **23**/15
ear-ring **23**/9
earth **1**/8
easy **46**
egg **12**/14
eight **48**; **51**
eighteen **51**
eighty **51**
elbow **22**/9
electric mixer **12**/15
elephant **38**/11
eleven **51**
empty **46**
engine **30**/9; **37**/8; **45**/11
exercise-book **9**/9
eye **23**/10
eyebrow **23**/2

Ff face **22**/2
factory **4**/2
fair **28**/2
fall **33**/3
family **24**
farm **2**/10; **3**
farmer **3**/4
fast **46**
fat **46**
father **24**/3
February **49**
fence **3**/8; **11**/7
ferry **29**/8
field **2**/9
fifteen **51**
fifty **51**
finger **22**/5
fire **26**; **26**/5
fire-engine **26**/8
fire-escape **26**/4
fire-hose **26**/13
fireman **26**/1
fireplace **14**/3
fish **38**/7
fishing **35**/7

fishing-boat **29**/1
five **48** ; **51**
flag **29**/3
flat **4**/1
floor **15**/15
flower **11**/12
flower-pot **11**/13
fly **36**/5; **39**/3
foot **22**/14
football **34**/1
footpath **10**/12
forest **2**/4
fork **11**/14; **13**/3
forty **51**
four **48**; **51**
fourteen **51**
freezer **5**/6
Friday **49**
fridge **12**/7
friend **21**/1
from **20**; **45**/5
front **44**/4; **46**
fruit **5**/2; **7**
frying-pan **12**/8
full **46**
fun **42**

Gg game **17**/14; **21**/7
garage **10**/10
garden **11**
gate **10**/13
girl **8**/4
give **42**/13
glass **13**/14
glasses **32**/5
glider **30**/1
glove **27**/10; **34**/15
glue **19**/11
go **45**
goal **34**/2
goat **3**/7
goggles **28**/10
good **46**
grandfather **24**/1
grandmother **24**/2
grape **7**/3

grass **11**/10
green **50**
grey **50**
grill **11**/2
group **40**/7
guitar **40**/12

Hh hair **23**/6
hairbrush **16**/10
hairdresser **4**/11
half **48**
hall **15**
hammer **19**/15
hand **22**/1; **42**/8
handbag **8**/13
handkerchief **32**/4
happy **46**
hard **46**
hat **27**/6
have **42**
head **22**/8; **23**
heavy **47**
hedge **3**/13
helicopter **30**/11; **31**/2
help **41**
hide **43**/14
high **47**
hill **2**/5
hit **36**/14
hole **31**/14
holiday **28**
horse **3**/1
hose **26**/13
hospital **32**
hot **47**
hotel **4**/10; **30**/5
hour **48**
house **10**
hug **42**/12
hundred **51**
husband **24**/10

Ii ice **8**/10
ice-cream **21**/9
in **2**; **4**; **5**; **6**; **7**; **8**; **9**; **12**; **17**; **30**;
      44/4

in front of **44**/7
injection **32**/7
inside **44**/4
into **1**; **45**/7
iron **19**/1; **41**/5
is **48**; **49**
island **31**/5
it **48**

Jj jacket **25**/9
jam **13**/12
January **49**
jeans **25**/10
jet engine **30**/9
jigsaw **17**/13
judo **35**/2
jug **13**/2
July **49**
jump **36**/6
June **49**

Kk keeper **38**/12
kettle **12**/10
key **37**/12
kick **36**/8
kiss **42**/2
kitchen **12**
kite **30**/4
knee **22**/12
knife **13**/10
knitting-needle **14**/4

Ll ladder **11**/4; **26**/3
lake **2**/2
lamp **14**/1
lamp-post **6**/6
land **29**/9
large **39**
laugh **42**/3
launch-pad **1**/12
lavatory **18**/1
lavatory-paper **18**/2
leaf **11**/3
left **47**
leg **22**/13; **44**/8
lemon **7**/7

letter **20**/1
letter-box **20**/6
lettuce **7**/8
lick **43**/9
lie **33**/6
lifeboat **29**/13
lift **32**/1
light **15**/3; **47**
lightning **27**/4
light-switch **15**/5
line **34**/3
liner **29**/4
lion **38**/6
lip **23**/13
listen **43**/13
little **46**
living-room **14**
long **47**
lorry **6**/3
low **47**
luck **33**
luggage **37**/13

Mm make **19**
man **8**/11
map **9**/1
March **49**
May **49**
meat **5**/7
medicine **32**/11
microphone **40**/8
midnight **48**
milk **12**/13; **20**/15
million **51**
minute **48**
mirror **18**/3
mixer **12**/15
Monday **49**
money **30**/14
monkey **38**/14
month **48**; **49**
moon **1**/6
moth **39**/5
mother **24**/4
motor-bike **37**/6
motor-boat **29**/12

motor-racing **35**/11
motorway **37**/2
mountain **2**/1
mouse **39**/10
moustache **23**/8
mouth **23**/5
mug **13**/1
mummy **24**/4
music **40**; **40**/14
my **22**; **23**

Nn nail **19**/14
name **20**/7
neck **23**/11
needle **14**/4
net **28**/7; **34**/9
new **47**
newspaper **32**/8
night **16**
nightie **16**/3
nine **51**
nineteen **51**
ninety **51**
noon **48**
nose **23**/7
nought **51**
November **49**
number **51**
number-plate **37**/14
nurse **32**/2
nut **7**/15

Oo o'clock **48**
October **49**
octopus **39**/14
off **45**/10
old **47**
on **3**; **29**; **44**/11
one **51**
onion **7**/14
onto **45**/9
open **41**/4; **47**
orange **7**/6; **50**
orbit **1**/7
out of **45**/8
outside **44**/5

oven **12**/3
over **45**/2

Pp paint **17**/11; **41**/3
pair **46**; **47**
pan **12**/9
panda **38**/15
pants **25**/5
paper **17**/12
parachute **30**/3
parcel **20**/5
park **8**
party **21**
pass **36**/13
passenger **30**/15
past **45**/11; **48**
path **2**/11
patient **32**/10
pavement **6**/15
pear **7**/2
pedestrian crossing **6**/11
pen **9**/14
pencil **9**/13
penguin **38**/13
penknife **19**/10
pepper **13**/7
petrol-pump **6**/5
petrol-station **6**/4
photograph **32**/9
piano **40**/10
pick up **33**/7
picnic **28**/6
picture **15**/4
pig **3**/14
pill **32**/12
pillow **16**/7
pilot **31**/3
pin **19**/2
pineapple **7**/5
pink **50**
pipe **10**/6
planet **1**/10
plant **15**/6; **41**/10
plaster **32**/15
plate **13**/5
platform **17**/6; **45**/9

play 42/10
player 34/5; 40/2
playground 4/8
pocket 25/11
police-car 26/11
policeman 26/12
police-station 6/1
pond 2/15
pop group 40/7
porter 45/12
post 43/10
post-box 20/6
postcard 20/4
poster 17/1
postman 20/2
post office 4/6; 20
pot 11/13
potato 7/13
pour 41/2
pram 8/15
present 21/2
puddle 27/15
pull 41/13
pump 20/11
pupil 9/5
puppet 21/5
purple 50
purse 5/11
push 41/11
put away 41/1
pyjamas 16/6

Qq quarter 48

Rr rabbit 3/10
racket 34/10
radio 14/15
raft 29/11
railway 45/3
rain 27/5
rainbow 27/1
raincoat 27/13
read 43/11
record 21/13; 40/15
recorder 40/4
record-player 21/14

red 50
rescue 31
restaurant 4/5
ride 36/4
right 47
ring 28/8
river 2/7
road 6/9; 37
rock 31/15
rocket 1/1
roof 10/3
rope 31/6
rope-ladder 11/4
round 45/12
roundabout 37/3
rowing 35/15
rowing-boat 29/7
rubber 9/12
rug 16/13
rugby 35/6
ruler 9/10
run 36/15
runway 30/12

Ss sad 46
sail 31/9; 36/2
sailor 31/7
salt 13/6
sand 28/15
satchel 9/15
satellite 1/9
Saturday 49
saucer 14/9
saw 19/9
scales 18/9
scarf 8/3
school 4/10
scissors 19/4
screw 19/12
screwdriver 19/13
sea 29; 31/10
seaside 28
seat 37/11
seat-belt 37/10
see-saw 11/8
second 48

September 49
seven 48; 51
seventeen 51
seventy 51
sew 41/9
sewing-machine 19/3
shake (hands) 42/8
shampoo 18/13
shark 39/13
sharp 46
shed 10/15
sheep 3/6
sheet 16/5
shelf 5/4
shell 28/4
ship 31/8
shirt 25/15
shoe 25/14
shoelace 25/13
shoot 36/7
shop 4/14
short 47
shorts 25/6
shout 42/6
shower 18/11
shut 41/15; 47
signpost 37/1
sing 42/9
singer 40/6
sink 12/11
sister 24/6
sit 33/12
six 48; 51
sixteen 51
sixty 51
skating 35/1
ski-ing 35/12
skirt 25/12
sky 27/2; 30
sleep 43/4
slice 21/12
slide 11/9
slipper 16/12
slow 46
small 39
smile 42/14

smoke 26/2
snake 38/5
snow 8/9
snowman 8/2
soap 18/12
sock 25/3
sofa 14/5
soldier 17/15
son 24/12
space 1
space-shuttle 1/2
space-station 1/13
space-suit 1/5
spade 11/15; 28/13
spider 39/6
sponge 18/15
spoon 13/8
sport 34; 35; 36
staircase 15/8
stairs 44/2, 9
stamp 20/9
stand 33/4
star 1/11
station 17/7; 45/7, 8
sting 33/15
stir 41/3
stool 14/14; 40/11
storm 31/1
stream 2/14
street 6
stretcher 32/14
string 20/3; 40/9
strong 47
submarine 29/7
suitcase 37/15
sun 1/3
Sunday 49
sun-glasses 28/9
supermarket 5
sweater 25/8
sweep 41/14
sweets 5/10
swim 36/10
swimming 35/4
swimming-costume 28/11
swimming-pool 35/5

swimming-trunks **28**/12
swing **11**/6; **42**/4
switch **15**/5

Tt T-shirt **25**/1
table **13**/4
table tennis **35**/10
tail **44**/7
tanker **29**/2
tap **18**/5
tea **5**/12
teacher **9**/2
team **34**/4
teapot **14**/7
tear **33**/13
telephone **15**/7
telephone-box **6**/7
television **14**/2
ten **48**; **51**
tennis **34**/7
tent **2**/13
they **45**
thin **46**
thing **19**; **43**
thirteen **51**
thirty **51**
thousand **51**
three **48**; **51**
through **45**/1
throw **36**/9
thumb **22**/6
Thursday **49**
ticket **30**/13

tie **33**/14
tiger **38**/3
time **48**; **49**
to **31**; **45**/4; **48**
toast **13**/13
toe **22**/15
toilet **18**/1
toilet-paper **18**/2
tongue **23**/3
tooth **23**/14
toothbrush **18**/4
toothpaste **18**/6
top **44**/2
torch **17**/9
towel **18**/8
town **4**
toys **17**/2
track suit **35**/15
tractor **3**/5
traffic-light **6**/12
train **17**/8; **45**/10
trainers **35**/14
tray **14**/10
tree **11**/1
trolley **5**/8
trousers **25**/2
truck **17**/4
trumpet **40**/1
T-shirt **25**/1
Tuesday **49**
tug **29**/5
tummy **22**/4
tunnel **45**/1

turn **41**/17
twelve **51**
twenty **48**; **51**
twenty-one **51**
two **51**
tyre **20**/14

Uu ugly **46**
umbrella **27**/12
uncle **24**/7
under **45**/6
up **44**/10
upstairs **10**/4

Vv vacuum-cleaner **15**/11
valley **2**/3
van **6**/14
vegetables **5**/1; **7**
vest **25**/4
village **2**/6
violin **40**/3

Ww wake **43**/5
walk **36**/3
wall **15**/2
wash **41**/8
washing-line **10**/14
washing-machine **12**/4
wasp **39**/4
waste-paper basket **14**/11
watch **32**/3
water **26**/7
wave **31**/12; **42**/1

we **44**
weak **47**
weather **27**
Wednesday **49**
week **48**; **49**
wet **47**
whale **39**/12
what **48**; **49**
wheel **20**/13
wheel-barrow **11**/11
where **44**; **45**
white **50**
wife **24**/11
wind **27**/7
window **10**/5; **44**/5
wing **30**/10
woman **8**/12
wood **2**/8
wool **14**/13
world **1**/8
worm **39**/9
write **33**/11

Xx

Yy year **48**
yellow **50**
young **47**

Zz zero **51**
zip **19**/7
zoo **38**

索引

下面每個字之後以黑體印刷的數字是頁碼，另一個數字則表示那個字在該頁裏的位置。例如'椅子13/15'表示'椅子'一字是第13頁的第15個字。

一畫

一51
一月49
一百51
一千51
一百萬51

二畫

二51
二十51
二十一51
二月49
七51
七十51
七月49
八51
八十51
八月49
九51
九十51
九月49
十51
十一51
十二51
十三51
十四51
十五51
十六51
十七51
十八51
十九51
十月49
十一月49
十二月49
十字路口6/13
刀13/10
人造衞星1/9

三畫

三51
三十51
三月49
大46
大衣27/9
大象38/11
大廈4/1
大拇指22/6
大頭針19/2
大小動物39
小46
小刀19/10
小時48
小孩8/7
小徑2/11，10/12
小溪2/14
小鳥3/12
小山丘2/5
小提琴40/3
小型貨車6/14
小髒水潭27/15
山2/1
山谷2/3
山羊3/7
工廠4/2
工具房10/15
女人8/12
女兒24/13
女孩8/4
上……45/9
下……45/10
下巴23/1
口23/5
口袋25/11
丈夫24/10
叉13/3
土兵17/15

四畫

太陽1/3
太空人1/4
太空衣1/5
太空艙1/15
太空基地1/13
太空穿梭機1/2
太平梯26/4
太陽眼鏡28/9
火26/5
火警26
火箭1/1
火爐14/3
火車17/8
火車站17/7
水26/7
水果5/2
水果和蔬菜7
水龍頭18/5
月48
月份49
月亮1/6
月台17/6
天空27/2
天虹27/1
天線10/1
天花板15/1
手22/1
手指22/5
手臂22/7
手帕32/4
手套27/10，34/15
手袋8/13
手推車5/8
牙齒23/14
牙刷18/4
牙膏18/6
牙醫4/13
牛油13/11
牛奶12/13，20/15
牛仔褲25/10
公共汽車6/10
公共汽車停車站6/8
毛巾18/8
毛毯16/4
毛線14/13
毛線衫25/8
木偶21/5
木筏29/11
五51
五十51
五月49
六51
六十51
六月49
什麼日期49
分48
日48
午夜48

五畫

四51
四十51
四月49
左47
右47
白50
白天的睡房裏17
母牛3/11
母親24/4
兄弟24/5
打開41/4
打氣筒20/11
甲板31/13
甲蟲39/7
生日會上21
卡片21/15
生菜7/8
巧克力8/1
奶油13/11
付賬處5/9
外衣25/9
石頭31/15
司機37/9
他們往哪裏去45
正午48
田2/9

六畫

在郊外2
在農場3
在市鎮4
在超級市場5
在街上6
在公園8
在樓上10/4
在樓下10/8
在廚房12

父親24/3
尺9/10
包裹20/5
內褲25/5
人羣26/10
升降機32/1
不幸33
少47
引擎37/8

在海上29
在空中30
在路上37
在動物園38
在……旁44/1
在……頂44/2
在……上44/3
在……裏44/4
在……外44/5
在……44/6
在……前面44/7
在……後44/8
在……底下44/9
在上方44/10
在下方44/11
在……下面45/6
向……那邊去45/4
地球1/8
地圖9/1
地毯15/12，16/13
地板15/15
地址20/8
行星1/10
行李37/13
行人路6/15
行人過路處6/11
衣着25
衣帶27/8
衣箱37/15
衣連裙25/7
汗衫25/1
老47
老虎38/3
老鼠39/10
羊3/6
企鵝38/13
耳23/15
耳環23/9
冰8/10
冰淇淋21/9
舌頭23/3
吃43/6
肉5/7
池塘2/15
帆31/9
划艇35/13
乒乓球35/10
交通燈6/12

安全帶37/10
托盤14/10
字紙簍14/11
收音機14/15
好46
光明47
灰50
年48

七畫
車輪20/13
車房10/10
車牌37/14
汽車37/7
汽油站6/4
汽油泵6/5
男人8/11
男孩8/6
沙28/15
沙發14/5
冷47
冷藏櫃5/6
快46
快樂46
困難46
坐33/12
吹42/15
吻42/2
步行36/3
投寄43/10
足球34/1
豆7/11
吸塵機15/11
貝殼28/4
我的身體22
肘22/9
伯24/7
妻子24/11
我們在哪裏44

八畫
花11/12
花園11
花灑18/11
雨27/5
雨傘27/12
雨衣27/13
牀16/2

牀單16/5
枕頭16/7
抽屜16/14
抽屜櫃16/15
拖鞋16/12
拖船29/5
拖拉機3/5
門10/9
門廳15
長47
長褲25/2
長途汽車37/4
油船29/2
油漆41/3
房子10
垃圾箱10/11
咖啡5/14
咖啡壺12/12
（電動）拌和機12/15
（無托）杯13/1
杯14/8
青瓜7/10
乳酪12/6
芝士12/6
果醬13/12
刷子15/13
玩具17/2
肥皂18/12
拉鍊19/7
明信片20/4
姓名20/7
朋友21/1
姊妹24/6
叔24/7
姑丈24/7
姑母24/8
表親24/9
兒子24/12
兔3/10
狗8/8
河流2/7
斧26/14
空中小姐30/7
直升機30/11，31/2
直笛40/4
板球34/13
弦40/9
拉41/13

拍手42/5
呼喊42/6
玩耍42/10
抱42/12
刷43/1
爬43/15
注射32/7
刺痛33/15
空46
肥46

九畫
星1/11
星期48，49
星期日49
星期一49
星期二49
星期三49
星期四49
星期五49
星期六49
洗41/8
洗衣機12/4
洗碗盆12/11
洗手盆18/7
洗髮劑18/13
洋葱7/14
洋娃娃21/6
洋娃娃屋19/8
飛機36/6
飛行36/5
香蕉7/4
胡蘿蔔7/12
胡椒粉13/7
風27/7
風暴31/1
姨丈24/7
姨母24/8
架5/4
屋頂10/3
柵門10/13
（花）盆11/13
玻璃杯13/14
客車廂17/5
拼圖17/13
軍人17/15
信20/1
背22/10

背心25/4
面頰23/12
建築物26/6
舢舨29/15
降落傘30/3
洞31/14
相片32/9
拾起33/7
美麗46
前46
後46
重47
紅50
穿過……45/1
秒48
界線34/3
柔道35/2
射36/7
看守員38/12
音樂40
活動43
咬43/8

十畫
海31/10
海浪31/12
海灘29/10
海員31/7
海邊度假28
海報17/1
海綿18/15
海豚38/8
浴室18
浴缸18/14
浴室地墊18/10
馬3/1
馬車3/2
馬鈴薯7/13
馬戲表演28/1
紙17/12
紙鳶30/4
紙皮盒15/10
書架9/6
書本9/7
書桌9/8
書包9/15
茶5/12
茶壺14/7

茶杯碟14/9
消防員26/1
消防水管26/13
祖父24/1
祖母24/2
草11/10
草叉11/14
烤架12/2
烤爐12/3
烤麵包片13/13
流血33/10
流行樂隊40/7
酒店4/10，30/5
瓶子5/15
粉筆9/3
粉紅50
座燈14/1
座椅37/11
烟26/2
烟囱10/2
起居室14
（織）針14/4
畚箕15/14
釘19/14
氣球21/8，30/2
胸22/3
唇23/13
家庭24
閃電27/1
旅行28/6
乘客30/15
島31/5
病人32/10
高速公路37/2
站立33/4
倒41/2
哭泣33/8
笑42/3
容易46
高47

十一畫
郵差20/2
郵筒20/6
郵票20/9
郵輪29/4
郵政局4/6
球34/6

球門34/2
球隊34/4
球員34/5
球場34/8
球網34/9
球拍34/10
球棒34/14
接球36/11
拳擊35/9
救援31
救火車26/8
救生艇29/13
救護車26/9
清潔41/6，46
清掃41/14
雪8/9
雪人8/2
魚38/7
魚網28/7
章魚39/14
蚯蚓39/9
蛇38/5
唱42/9
唱機21/14
唱片21/13，40/15
蛋12/14
蛋糕21/11
蛋糕片21/12
眼23/10
眼眉23/2
眼鏡32/5
麥克風40/8
做夢43/3
做手工19
釣魚35/7
貨車6/3
貨卡17/4
貨櫃船29/6
厠所18/1
厠紙18/2
剪刀19/4
船31/8
船長29/14
理髮店4/11
帳幕2/13
控制室1/14
商店4/14
停車場4/15

梨7/2
堅果7/15
教師9/2
（繩）梯11/4
匙13/8
晚上的睡房裏16
晨衣16/1
梳16/11，43/2
掛錶32/3
從郵政局出來20
軟帽27/11
桶28/14
陸地29/9
票30/13
紮33/14
強壯47
虛弱47
乾47
紫50
從……那邊來45/5
推41/11
舔43/9

十二畫
游泳35/4，36/10
游泳池35/5
游泳衣28/11
游泳褲28/12
黑50
黑暗47
黑板9/4
黃50
黃蜂39/4
雲27/3
雲梯26/3
椅子13/15
椅墊14/6
窗10/5
窗簾16/8
畫15/4
畫筆17/10
（燈）開關15/5
開着的47
短47
短褲25/6
跑36/15
跑道30/12
進入……45/7

進入太空1
發射台1/12
湖2/2
森林2/4
圍牆3/8，11/7
街角6/2
菠蘿7/5
植物15/6
提袋9/11
筆9/14
鈕扣19/6
帽27/6
報紙32/8
堡壘17/3
惡劣的天氣27
渡船29/8
猴子38/14
棒球34/12
揚帆36/2
喇叭40/1
結他40/12
尋樂趣42
割傷33/9
跌下33/3
揮手42/1
握手42/8
給42/13
鈍46
藍50
棕50
幾點鐘48

十三畫
運動34，35，36
運動鞋35/14
運動衣35/15
運行軌道1/7
電筒17/9
電話15/7
電話亭6/7
電視機14/2
電冰箱12/7
電影院4/3
遊戲21/7
（硬紙板）遊戲17/14
遊樂場4/8
遊藝會28/2
腳22/14

腳趾22/15
腳踏車20/12
農人3/4
農場2/10
鄉村2/6
路6/6　　9
路標37/1
葡萄7/3
椰菜7/9
鉛筆9/13
矮47
矮樹11/5
滑梯11/9
滑雪35/12
滑翔機30/1
煎鍋12/8
壺13/2
碗13/9
睡袍16/3
睡衣16/6
睡覺43/4
煞車20/10
腹22/4
舅父24/7
舅母24/8
裙25/12
圓環28/8
艇31/11
携帶33/5
綁33/14
新47
零51
經過……45/11
溜冰35/1
跳水36/1
跳高36/6
跳舞42/11
傳球36/13
獅子38/6
蛾39/5
鼓40/5
微笑42/14
飲43/7
飲品28/5
躲藏43/14

十四畫
銀行4/9

領巾8/3
管10/6
晾衣繩10/14
碟13/5
凳14/14，40/11
餅乾21/3
腿22/13
鼻23/7
漁船29/1
旗29/3
對比46
骯髒46
慢46
滿46
瘦46
輕47
綠50
網球34/7
熊38/10
熊貓38/15
蜜蜂39/1
蒼蠅39/3
蜘蛛39/6
歌手40/6
種植41/10

十五畫
膠水19/11
膠布32/15
膠套靴27/14
駕車36/12
駕駛員31/3
鞋25/14
鞋帶25/13
樂師40/2
樂曲40/14
熨斗19/1
熨衣服41/5
麵包5/3
課室裏9
練習簿9/9
靠手椅14/12
樓梯15/8
鬧鐘16/9
髮刷16/10
磅18/9
線19/5
輪胎20/14

膝 22/12
嘴巴 23/5
髭（嘴上的鬍子）23/8
潛水艇 29/7
摩托車 37/6
摩托船 29/12
噴射引擎 30/9
蝴蝶 39/2
躺 33/6
踢 36/8
寫字 33/11
撕破 33/13
銳利 46
憂愁 46
熱 47
數目 51

十六畫
樹 11/1
樹枝 11/2
樹葉 11/3
樹林 2/8
樹籬 3/13
餐廳 4/5
餐檯 13/4
餐桌上 13
燈 15/3
燈柱 6/6
學校 4/4
學生 9/5
頭 22/8
頭髮 23/6
頸 23/11

橙 7/6，50
豬 3/14
鴨 3/15
蔬菜 5/1
糖果 5/10
獨木舟 28/3
獨輪車 11/11
機場 30/8
機翼 30/10
錢 30/14
錢包 5/11
橋 8/5
橡皮 9/12
磚 10/7
燒水壺 12/10
鋸 19/9
錘子 19/15
擔架 32/14
橫過……45/2，45/3
駱駝 38/9
螞蟻 39/8
貓 39/11
鋼琴 40/10
錄音帶 40/13
醒 43/5

十七畫
嬰兒 8/14
嬰兒車 8/15
縫紉 41/9
縫紉機 19/3
螺絲釘 19/12
螺絲起子 19/13

篷車 2/12
鮮肉店 4/12
擱板 5/4
鍋 12/9
牆 15/2
臉 22/2
臀部 22/11
繃帶 32/13
營 33/1
醜陋 46
濕 47
點鐘 48
賽車 35/11
擊球 36/14
環形交叉處 37/3
幫忙 41

十八畫
騎馬 36/4
騎腳踏車 35/3
醫生 32/6
醫院裏 32
繩 20/3
繩索 31/6
顏色 50
顏料 17/11
雞 3/9
檸檬 7/7
鞦韆 11/6
禮物 21/2
嬸母 24/8
斷 33/2
舊 47

離開……45/8
繞過……45/12
擲 36/9
鎖匙 37/12
鯊魚 39/13
儲放 41/1
轉動 41/7
擺動 42/4

十九畫
藥房 4/7
藥水 32/11
藥丸 32/12
關閉 41/15
關閉的 47
蹺蹺板 11/8
鏟 11/15，28/13
櫥櫃 15/9
鏡子 18/3
鬍鬚 23/4
壞 46
鯨 39/12
蟹 39/15
攀爬 42/7
繪畫 43/12

二十畫
警察 26/12
警車 26/11
警署 6/1
籃子 5/5
籃球 34/11
蘋果 7/1

爐 12/1
鐘 26/15
懸崖 31/4

二十一畫
護士 32/2
護目鏡 28/10
護頭盔 37/5
騾 3/3
顧客 5/13
攝影機 21/4
蠟燭 21/10
襪 25/3

二十二畫
襯衫 25/15
籠 38/2
讀 43/11
聽 43/13

二十三畫
體育運動 35/8
攪拌 41/12

二十四畫
鷹 38/1
鹽 13/6
罐頭 12/5

二十五畫
欖球 35/6

二十七畫
鱷魚 38/4